BRAIN
BOOK

Charles Phillips

BRAIN
BOOK

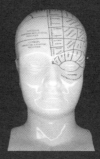

MENTAL GYMNASTICS
to TRAIN YOUR BRAIN

METRO BOOKS
NEW YORK

Metro Books
122 Fifth Avenue
New York, NY 10011

*   ISBN 978-1-4351-0613-0

Printed and bound in China

3   5   7   9   10   8   6   4   2

CONTENTS

Introduction 7

UNDERSTANDING YOUR BRAIN 11

    Mixed puzzles. 32

    Perception puzzles 42

    Language puzzles 56

    Number puzzles 60

    Emotion puzzles 66

    Memory puzzles 76

    Logic puzzles 92

    Lateral thinking puzzles. 104

    Intuition puzzles 112

BRAIN TRAINING. **115**

    Left/right-brain exercises. **130**

    Music exercises. **136**

    Visualization exercises & puzzles **142**

    Language exercises & puzzles. **152**

    Number exercises & puzzles. **162**

    Memory exercises & puzzles **176**

BRAIN WORKOUT. **187**

The answers **218**

Suggested reading **237**

Notes and scribbles. **238**

Acknowledgements **240**

Introduction

Remember how we were once told that our mental ability peaks at around age 18–24 and that it would be downhill from then on? We were warned that heading a ball during a game of soccer or drinking too much would accelerate our decline by killing neurons. We were told that if neural networks (webs of connected brain cells) were destroyed, they could never be remade. All this, it turns out, is untrue.

Scientists now know that the brain is a regenerating organ. If we use it, if we keep our brain cells firing and making new connections, then its powers will not dwindle. Even in our mature years, the brain can repair and regenerate itself. Your future is bright.

With this in mind, welcome to the *Brain Book*, the key to keeping your brain trim and your thinking lively. This little book contains a wealth of scientific facts about the brain, to help you appreciate just how powerful your thinking organ is and what astonishing feats it's capable of. And it's also full of specially designed puzzles and exercises that will challenge your brain and give it the training it deserves. Working your way through this book will help you achieve peak mental performance – whatever your age.

Fulfil your potential The typical brain has ten billion brain cells. When you think, when you learn something new, you forge connections within your brain. Each of your neurons connects an average ten thousand times with other brain cells, making a staggering total of one hundred thousand billion connections. Indeed, there are more connections in your brain than there are stars in the Milky Way galaxy.

TACKLING THE PUZZLES
Throughout the book you will find puzzles and exercises designed to get different parts of your brain in gear. The more straightforward puzzles are rated as one bar (*see bottom left*), but the rating of five bars (*see bottom right*) is reserved for only the most difficult of challenges.

As scientists have come to a more accurate understanding of the brain, they have realized that the potential of our thinking organ is truly staggering. The number of connections we are capable of forming is colossal. One estimate, made by Pyotr Anokhin and quoted by expert Tony Buzan, is the number 1 followed by ten million kilometres (six million miles) of 0s. So the potential connections outnumber atoms in the universe. This should give you some idea of your potential.

We are getting younger If you are of mature years, you may be younger than you think! In terms of life expectancy you are younger than your grandfather or mother was at your age. Moreover, armed with the latest knowledge on how your brain works, you have a much better chance than your grandparents had of keeping fully alert in later life. So read through the *Brain Book* and prepare to marvel at the power of your grey matter.

Neuroscientists and brainpower experts will also tell you that your perceptions – the way you see reality – are among the most important elements of your thinking. If you believe 'I am getting older and feeling tired, my memory is beginning to fail and my mind is falling apart', then you'll probably begin to make these imagined effects real. But if you think, 'Whatever age I am, my mind can be alert and fully stimulated if I take the trouble to keep it active', you have already started to protect your brain from decline.

The *Brain Box* puzzle The wooden puzzle in the box consists of a neat six-sided cube, made from 27 smaller cubes. Unravelling it is easy, but fitting it back together is quite a challenge! The puzzle provides a good visual–spatial workout – helping your ability to think in three dimensions – as well as boosting your overall powers of thought. To solve it, you will need patience and imagination to find fresh perspectives.

> **THINK YOUNG!**
> Research shows that over-65s can reduce their mental age by 14 years through brain training with problem-solving and puzzles.

UNDERSTANDING YOUR BRAIN

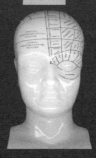

To get the most out of training the brain, we need a little background knowledge. What is thinking? Why do we feel emotions? How does memory work? What are lateral thinking and intuition? This know-how will help us plan a mental gymnastics routine to stretch the brain's many high-powered capabilities.

A short history of the brain

Our early ancestors did not associate the brain with memory, intelligence and other mental faculties – they thought of the mind rather as a disembodied spirit. The ancient Egyptians, for example, revered the heart as the centre of intelligence and saw the brain largely as an unimportant organ.

In the first millennium BCE the ancient Greeks were the first to link the brain with the mind: in the 6th century BCE Alcmaeon declared that intelligence resided in the brain, while in the 5th century BCE, Plato suggested that the brain recorded impressions from experience, like mouldings pressed in soft wax. But his most famous student, Aristotle, followed the Egyptians in believing that the heart was the organ of thought while the brain's job was to cool the blood.

Herophilus, a Greek anatomist working in the north African city of Alexandria in the 4th–3rd centuries BCE, identified the brain's ventricles (spaces in the brain that carry protective and nourishing cerebrospinal fluid) as the locus of our thinking power. This theory was taken up in the 2nd century

CE by Galen of Pergamum, then transmitted to Europe by Arab physicians and generally accepted for hundreds of years.

The nervous system Only in the 18th and 19th centuries did researchers begin to understand the brain's role in the nervous system; some, including the German anatomist Franz Gall, drew maps tracing which part of the brain was linked to which activity. But by the mid-20th century this model had been shown to be too simple – and scientists such as Karl Spencer Lashley were arguing that the whole brain was involved in the more complex processes of the mind.

But much remained hidden. The brain's awesome power, self-regenerating capacity and almost limitless expandability were secrets waiting to be discovered.

NEW MODEL BRAIN
In evolutionary terms, the brain is a recent invention. Life on Earth dates back 4,500 million years, *Homo sapiens* are three million years old, but the modern brain evolved only 50,000 years ago.

What is the brain?

The brain is the body's control centre. Not only does it run complex mental activities, such as learning a foreign language or doing mind-bending puzzles, it also controls your digestion, breathing and other largely subconscious body functions, and commands your deliberate physical actions such as working out at the gym. This prodigiously powerful organ weighs on average 1.5 kg (3 lb) in a man and 1.25 kg (2 lb 12 oz) in a woman – a difference due to the average variation in body size between the sexes.

Most of your mind's processes are controlled in the cerebral cortex – the wrinkled surface of the brain that looks like a walnut. The cortex, which covers the brain's largest part, the cerebrum, is 'cell-heavy': despite taking up only one-quarter of brain volume, it contains 75 per cent of its cells.

THIRSTY WORKER
Although the average brain accounts for just one-fiftieth of an adult's body weight, it uses a fifth of the oxygen in the blood.

The brain contains left and right hemispheres. These are cross-wired: the right hemisphere controls the left side of the body, while the left half commands the body's right side. Researchers have also shown that the 'right brain' appears to control artistic activities, while the 'left brain' commands logic, maths (math [Amer]) and language (*see pages 124–9*).

Each hemisphere has four areas called 'lobes'. The frontal lobes control thought and planning. The other lobes – at the side, top and rear – help control the senses and govern language. Scientists also sometimes distinguish between 'the upper brain' (the cerebral cortex), which directs mental activities, and the 'lower brain' (including the midbrain, cerebellum and brainstem), which primarily control bodily functions, emotions, sexual urges, and instincts such as the 'fight or flight' response, which prepares us for action when we perceive danger. The upper brain appeared at a later evolutionary stage and is sometimes called the 'new brain'.

The latest research indicates that most mental activities involve many different parts of the brain working together.

How brain cells connect

Your brain contains an amazing ten billion cells, called neurons. Each cell has a round centre containing its nucleus, with a cluster of tentacles at one end like the branches of a tree (called 'dendrites', from the Greek for 'tree') and at the other end a long shoot called an 'axon'. The axon branches out at the end to make connections with other cells. These connections are actually made across tiny gaps called synapses. A cell sends information in the form of electrical impulses along its axon, generating a chemical transfer across the synapse to another brain cell. The process sparks a reaction in the cells, creating a network of connected cells.

Making new connections The crucial thing to know is that when you learn something new you make new connections between cells, forging new neural pathways. This improves your general mental powers. Researchers have identified more than fifty different chemical messengers ('neurotransmitters') involved in the lightning-quick movement of information through circuits of brain cells. When we alter our 'brain chemistry' by having a coffee or a couple of glasses of wine we alter the activities of these chemical messengers.

Brainwaves The more you use your upper brain, the more the brain cells are firing, and the more electricity the brain generates. Using electroencephalograph (EEG) machines, researchers have identified four levels of electrical activity, each distinguished by a pattern of brainwaves. When alert and fully engaged, your brain emits beta brainwaves (14 to 40 cycles per second). At rest after activity, you have alpha brainwaves (9 to 14 cycles). Theta brainwaves (5 to 8 cycles) occur when you are 'on automatic', while delta brainwaves (1.5 to 4 cycles) occur only in deep, dreamless sleep.

BRAIN CHEMISTRY
Every second, an astounding 100,000 chemical reactions take place in your brain. The electrical impulse sent by a neuron lasts 1/1000th of a second and travels at up to 200 mph.

17

A history of games

From time immemorial people have enjoyed the challenge of mental tests, puzzles and games. Small clay labyrinths like tiny mazes were popular with the ancient Indus civilization of northern India and Pakistan in around 2600 BCE. At about the same time, the inhabitants of the ancient Mesopotamian city of Ur played board games similar to Ludo. In ancient Egypt (from the 2nd millennium BCE on) people passed the time with games like backgammon.

The oldest surviving puzzle is the loculus – attributed to Archimedes, the 3rd-century BCE Greek mathematician. Players rearrange fourteen shapes to form a square or other formations. It is extremely difficult, so is also known as the *stomachion*, the 'maddening problem'. The ancient Chinese played a related seven-piece puzzle called the tangram.

Over the centuries, human ingenuity and love of games fired the development of a dazzling variety of games and puzzles. Many derived from teaching tools. The jigsaw puzzle, for instance, developed from the 'dissected maps' made by 18th-century London engraver/map-maker John Spilsbury. The celebrated Rubik's cube came from a puzzle developed by Hungarian Ernö Rubik in the 1970s to help architectural students practise three-dimensional visualization (did you know there are forty-three billion billion possible arrangements of the Rubik's cube?).

Other puzzles were developed just for fun – like the crossword puzzle, developed by an English emigrant to the USA, Arthur Wynne, first published in *Fun*, on 21 December 1913. The British developed the much more difficult 'cryptic crossword'. The first, by 'Torquemada', was published on 30 July 1925 in the *Saturday Westminster*.

American pioneer Sam Loyd is remembered as America's greatest puzzle writer. He began publishing chess problems in the mid-1850s and progressed to mathematical and three-dimensional problems. He invented many types of maths brainteasers, published several compendium-books of puzzles and also worked as a ventriloquist.

Brain training

Human beings derive satisfaction from measuring up to a challenge, and most of us have a playful element somewhere in our characters that takes pleasure in games. Giving ourselves a mental workout is not only enjoyable, it is also beneficial for the brain and for our general health.

Noradrenalin is a chemical in the brain associated with stress. Too much can be damaging, making you anxious and overly alert so that you cannot sleep, and preventing your brain from functioning effectively. But a little stress – the kind provided by a challenging puzzle – is a good thing. Released in moderate amounts, noradrenalin improves the speed and effectiveness of connections between the brain cells.

So your mind functions better when you are slightly stressed. Meeting a challenge also boosts your physical health and general state of mind. The sense of achievement you feel at having mastered a difficult puzzle, say, is associated with the release of beneficial brain chemicals that lift your mood and raise the performance of your immune system.

Use it or lose it As we have seen, the former conventional wisdom – that we are doomed to gradual decline in our brain performance because our inborn supply of brain cells gradually dwindles year by year – is untrue. Doctors now know that the more we forge new connections between our brain cells, the better our mental performance will be. The most effective way to maintain brainpower is to use the brain and to provide it with fresh types of challenge.

Stimulate yourself Research in Chicago indicates that people with a mentally demanding job or a lifestyle that continues to provide them with real brain challenges, perhaps through doing puzzles and crosswords, are around 50 per cent less likely to succumb to Alzheimer's or other forms of dementia. Your brain stays young if you keep it active.

Meeting interesting people is another way to keep your brain alert. Scientists have shown that isolated animals have poorer mental functioning than those in a group. This applies particularly to human beings, who evolved as a 'social' species.

Ways of thinking

Do you ever think you are so different from your child or parents you may as well be a separate species? Well, children and teenagers *do* have quite different brains from older people.

Wiring matters For one thing the young are not fully wired – the brain's frontal lobes, which govern mental control processes, do not fully develop until the early-to-mid 20s. We are also the product of what we have thought. Firing and connecting brain cells, stimulated by experience and knowledge, create patterns of connections that change the brain permanently.

What are the effects of this on how we think? At different life stages we tend to have different 'thinking styles'. Children up to the age of twelve, for example, like to consider things in terms of concrete reality rather than abstract ideas. They recognize none of an adult's accepted boundaries and so can be extremely creative. They love to ask 'Why?'

Teenagers tend to have a highly developed sense of justice and of logic, and a desire to work out all the consequences. Driven by idealism, they do not understand the compromises that many adults have accepted. Like children, they question assumptions. They are fearless explorers of the mind.

The adult brain Adults have a wealth of experience and a brain wired with diverse connections at their disposal. They may have challenging work and a rich and varied life to keep them on their toes. The frontal lobes, now fully developed and functioning, give an enhanced capacity for self-control and foresight – predicting outcomes and adjusting activity accordingly. On the other hand, adults stuck in routine may find their memory failing or their powers of self-expression decaying. This is probably because they are not exercising these faculties. But there is no need for such mental decline.

Adults and pre-adults have plenty to learn from each other. Older thinkers can sometimes benefit from the unfettered, mind-bending approach of the young, while the less mature could sometimes do with adopting the focus and self-discipline shown by their older counterparts.

How to train your brain

The Irish playwright George Bernard Shaw declared: 'We don't stop playing because we grow old, we grow old because we stop playing.' You can choose from a wide variety of games and puzzles to give your brain the regular workout it needs to keep its neurons firing.

Visual and three-dimensional puzzles like printed mazes or the wooden puzzle included with this book help you to forge and reinforce neural pathways connected to visual and spatial awareness. Lateral thinking exercises are a way of developing creative problem-solving, the 'no boundaries' thinking of the 'young-at-mind'. Chess and backgammon boost strategic and counter-intuitive thinking. Attempting anagrams or crosswords or playing Scrabble™ reinforces your vocabulary and encourages you to practise creative thinking.

All these pastimes enable us to develop skills and thinking strategies that are useful in work and other day-to-day activities. And they are an investment for the future. Because by keeping our brains busy with challenging and unfamiliar problems, we are greatly increasing the likelihood that our faculties will stay sharp far into old age.

'Work hard, play hard' Novelty is key – keeping day-to-day life fresh and surprising helps us stay alert. Repetition makes us less attentive, but when we try something different we often feel more alive and more engaged.

And according to the latest neuroscientific thinking, when we are engaged and attentive, we are boosting our brainpower. When we attend to something new and stimulating, not only do we make fresh connections between brain cells, but the brain also releases chemicals called neuromodulators, which reinforce these connections.

CHANGE YOUR PERSPECTIVE
Look for mind-stretching variety in your day-to-day life. Buy different newspapers to get a fresh perspective. Choose a novel by an author you have never read before. Download a few songs by a band you don't know. Or try meditation ...

Making sense of the world

We need a range of mental faculties to make sense of the world, to establish and maintain our self-image and to plot a path through daily life.

We have our general intelligence and powers of thought, which allow us to compare and classify, to sequence and compartmentalize. Using our general intelligence, we marshal logic, engage in lateral thinking and test the leadings of our intuition.

We have our perceptions – the brain's interpretation of what we see, hear, taste, feel and smell around us. In terms of our mental life, these are the raw material of thought.

We have language and numerical skills, which we use to describe and label the world and our own response to it. We have our emotions, generated in our lower brain, experienced through physiological effects such as a raised heartrate or breathlessness and interpreted as 'fear' or 'envy' in the upper brain. Emotions are deeply involved in even the most rational of thought processes (*see pages 62–3*).

And we have memory, which maintains a record of the past inscribed in millions of cross-wired, connected brain cells. In a sense the memory is the keeper of our identity. If we suffered a terrible emotional trauma or physical injury that deprived us of our memory, we would have to rebuild entirely our sense of who we are. And, unless the memories returned, we would never know whether we were essentially the same person as before, or not. Philosophers have spent many years discussing just such issues.

Brainpower In daily life we rely on the faculties working together. We make sense of our perceptions, emotions and memory using our linguistic capacity and general intelligence. But as we train our brains, each area can be developed and exercised separately. For this reason, in the following pages, the faculties of general thinking, perception, language, the emotions and memory are considered in detail one after the other, with creative and light-hearted puzzles tailored to develop skills and capacity in each area.

Learning to think

Some experts believe that the ability to think is a product of your general intelligence, and that this is determined by the genes you inherit. But there is increasing evidence to suggest that thinking is a skill learnt and practised.

IQ and other tests Intelligence Quotient tests – better known as IQ tests – claim to measure your general intelligence compared to other people of roughly the same age. They involve a set of standardized tests that measure visual–spatial, verbal, numerical, perceptual and other forms of intelligence. When first developed, such tests provided a measure of your 'mental age', and your IQ was worked out by dividing your mental age by your actual age, then multiplying by 100. Modern tests calculate your IQ level on the basis of statistical figures for intelligence levels in populations.

IQ tests are a vast, multi-million-dollar industry. But some modern psychologists doubt their accuracy and usefulness, arguing that intelligence cannot be measured neatly on a scale, and that the tests have been created without anyone defining the quality – 'intelligence' – that they claim to measure. Most tests, they suggest, measure what people have learnt rather than their mental potential, and many favour people from dominant cultural and racial groups.

Modern IQ tests were developed in the USA from the Binet-Simon Scale, devised in 1905 to identify children who needed extra help. Alfred Binet himself warned against using his scale for more general intelligence testing. He also argued that intelligence, far from being a fixed 'quantity' inherited from your ancestors, was a fluid and living ability that could be developed through practice and by learning relevant skills.

There is a growing consensus that you can improve thinking skills through doing mind-stretching puzzles and games.

PUSH YOURSELF!
Try something different – develop your skills in areas where you find it harder to perform and where, perhaps for that reason, you do not normally go.

Practice makes perfect

Here and now we have the capacity to hone our thinking skills, and increase our levels of mental alertness. All we need is the will to do it and the appropriate tools – such as the puzzles and exercises on the pages that follow.

It is common knowledge that if you don't use the muscles in your arms they grow weaker, whereas if you exercise them – in a gym workout, doing the housework, keeping the garden beautiful – they become stronger. Think of your brain as a muscle. It too needs a regular workout. To maintain good mental performance – to keep the memory sharp and thinking clear – use your brain in unusual and varied ways.

Variety is the spice of life Have you noticed that sometimes when you visit a new place on holiday, time seems to slow down? A few days is a satisfyingly long time. But when routine dominates your life, several weeks go by in a flash. This is because when you are immersed in fresh experiences, you are more attentive – and alive. Your brain is more engaged.

Do something different Take this opportunity to try something different. Puzzles have a way of surprising you, of stretching your thinking. This will keep you alert. But above all, have fun. Start by attacking the exercises on pages 32–5, which offer a gentle introduction to the joys of puzzling. Trying them out will tone your brain muscle. The more variety, the better the exercise for your brain – and the more new connections you will make among your brain cells.

That's why I recommend that you do puzzles and exercises you'd normally avoid. Tackle the number puzzles even if you think you can't add up. Enjoy the spot the differences even if you don't normally think of yourself as a perceptive person. You'll probably do better than you expect. And if not, keep trying.

TAP INTO YOUR POTENTIAL
Scientists suggest that even the most diligent and mind-bendingly brilliant people use less than 1 per cent of the capacity of their brains.

Puzzle 1 NUMBER PYRAMID

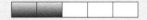

This numerical challenge needs a bit of logical reasoning. Each block in this pyramid is equal to the sum of the two numbers beneath it. Can you find all the missing numbers?

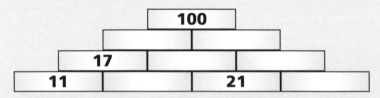

Puzzle 2 WORD POWER

Anagrams are a good test of your word power. Can you unravel this one to find a cartoon hero?

rome mops shin

Puzzle 3 SPOT THE DIFFERENCE

Often our eyes are tricked into seeing what we want to see. But those who are perceptive will be able to spot the seven differences between these two pictures. Circle them in the drawing on the right.

Puzzle 4 TIME TO EAT?

Three children are having lunch. Each has a different sandwich and a drink. Can you work out who ate what from the two clues given opposite? The box explains how best to tackle logic puzzles. Once you master the art you'll be able to use your brainpower to tackle more difficult puzzles and really stretch your logical mind. These puzzles are addictive!

	CHICKEN SANDWICH	HAM SANDWICH	CHEESE SANDWICH	ORANGE DRINK	LEMON DRINK	LIME DRINK
JOHN						
JULIE						
JERRY						
ORANGE DRINK						
LEMON DRINK						
LIME DRINK						

Puzzle 4 TIME TO EAT? (CLUES)

1 Jerry has a cheese sandwich but not a lemon drink.

2 Julie isn't the child with both an orange drink and a ham sandwich.

How to solve logic puzzles

The trick to solving logic puzzles lies in deducing what is known for sure from the information you've been given. First, unravel the information in the clues to work out what is valid and invalid, then deduce further information. It is useful to add ticks or crosses to the grid, as shown, according to what you know to be true or untrue.

	JANE	ANNA	LOUISE	RESTAURANT	BEACH	MUSEUM
MOTHER	✖					
FATHER	✖	✖			✖	
AUNT	✔					
RESTAURANT						
BEACH		✖				
MUSEUM						

In this example, three sisters are taken on an outing by either their Mother, Father or Aunt to either a restaurant, a beach or a museum. In this case we know that Jane wasn't taken out by her Mother or Father, so must have gone out with her Aunt. Anna didn't go out with her Father and she didn't go to the beach. Louise must therefore have gone out with her Father as none of the other girls did. In this way, using the clues, it is possible to deduce all the information you need to complete the grid.

What is perception?

Imagine a woman walking on a winter morning along a snowy lane. She looks up at the blue sky, and across at the tree branches, which appear starkly black against the whiteness of the snow-covered fields. As she walks, she hears the crunch of the snow beneath her feet and perhaps the song of a bird and the drone of an aeroplane. She feels the cold biting her hands when she takes her gloves off and tastes something of the frozen night still afloat on the winter air.

She experiences the morning through all her senses simultaneously. And when she does look, she is seeking patterns and meaning around her. Her brain interprets the flow of light photons hitting her retinas and 'creates' this winter postcard scene on the basis of known patterns in previous experience. A recently born baby, with still-developing eyesight and brain, would have a quite different experience of the flood of light, a quite different reality.

Many psychologists and philosophers declare perception to be the most important aspect of our thinking. Our way of seeing determines how we look at the world and what things we take into account. It determines the patterns we look for in sensory experience and information and therefore the meaning we extract from them.

This insight is liberating. It means we can change. And changing our perceptual mind-set transforms our way of seeing, in turn transforming our way of being. I may think 'I can't do mathematical problems'. But when I try them, I may find I am better than I anticipated – and certainly when I persevere with them, I will improve my level of skill.

Seeing patterns You have just taken delivery of a new car and invite your friend along for a trial run. As you drive, you notice several other drivers at the wheel of your make of car, some driving your model, others driving older ones. You mention this to your friend, who says she hasn't noticed. You realize that only a couple of weeks ago, before you bought this car, you probably wouldn't have noticed either. Your perception – your experience of reality – would have been different.

Varying perceptions

At the age of ten, the English poet William Blake told his father he had seen a group of angels in a tree in Peckham Rye, south London. Was he mad? Did he really see them? Had his father been with him at the time, would he have seen them?

'If the doors of perception were cleansed,' Blake wrote later, 'everything would appear to man as it is: Infinite.' He argued that we are prevented from seeing reality as it actually is by our habits of perception.

Religious mystics agree with Blake, declaring – on the basis of their own experience – that we see reality with imperfect vision, but that, perceived in a new way, or with our current way of seeing dramatically improved, the world appears unified, sacred, limitless, full of meaning. Most people, however, have a much more mundane view of life on Earth. Whose reality is real?

If angels exist, it is probable that only people who believe in them can see them. Not only do people sometimes have quite different perceptions of the same reality, but also – psychologists point out – they may not perceive something at all if it is completely unfamiliar, or does not fit in with their preconceptions. They may develop a 'blindness' for something that is there.

This is as true in the world of ideas as it is in the world of trees and Peckham Rye (and angels?). We may limit our capacity for problem-solving, adaptive reasoning and creative thinking – in the workplace, when discussing what is dear to us, or when playing games or doing puzzles – by having a fixed outlook. But reconsidering our perceptual framework, practising the skill of seeing things from a different perspective, may set us free from our preconceptions.

COLOUR 'BLINDNESS'

Colour 'blindness' is another example of how our way of seeing affects our 'reality'. In one of the most common forms, green and red look almost identical. So the realities of 'red' and 'green' dissolve for people with this condition.

Errors of perception

Our perception of reality is crucial to our thinking. Professor David Perkins of Harvard University has been undertaking research into thinking, learning, teaching and creativity since 1971. He has demonstrated that 90 per cent of errors in thinking arise from errors in perception.

An intelligent person might decide on a fixed belief, perhaps because of the power of inherited tradition, and then put all his or her intelligence to work in defending this belief. In the past, intelligent people supported widely held intellectual positions that we now despise – for example, that one race was superior to another, that there was nothing wrong in keeping slaves, or that human sacrifice was a sacred duty. Most of us would now say that those people's thinking was invalidated by their false perception of reality.

We may also find our logical thinking is undermined if we form an 'emotional attachment' to a position – perhaps because a friend thinks that way. Historians report that Queen Victoria favoured the Whig Party in politics because she believed that her beloved dead father (Edward Augustus, Duke of Kent) had supported the Whigs. She may have been right to do so – that is a matter for debate. But what is certain is that her decision did not have a sound basis.

'My eyes are playing tricks on me, again' Optical illusions provide a concrete and convincing demonstration of how our powers of perception can be fallible. They arise from the way our eyes and brain work together to make sense of the world around us. A golf ball close up can appear the same size as a football further away. When you're sitting in a train alongside another carriage and the other carriage starts moving forward, you may initially be unable to tell whether your train or the other carriage is moving.

The perceptual puzzles in the pages that follow provide some practice in shifting your perceptual frame, encouraging a fresh perspective for your seeing and your thinking. They will also help boost your general brainpower by forging new mental connections.

Puzzle 5 HARNESS YOUR EYES

By looking at the first two figures, can you plot the movement of the individual shapes in the third figure, to work out which of the five possible answers below is the correct one?

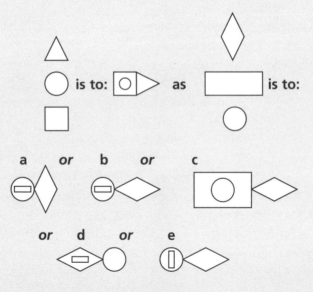

Puzzle 6 HEAP BIG PUZZLE

Can you trust your eyes? Are these pictures below really identical? At first glance, perhaps, but believe it or not there are eight differences between them. Your task is to circle them in the drawing on the right. As quickly as you can ...

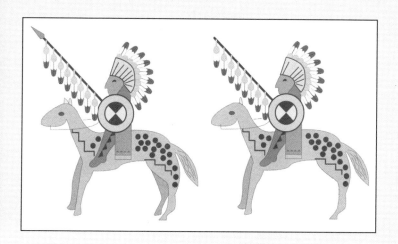

Puzzle 7 HAMMER HORROR

Brian the builder's identical hammer collection is in a mess.
Can you help him clear up and spot the odd hammer out?

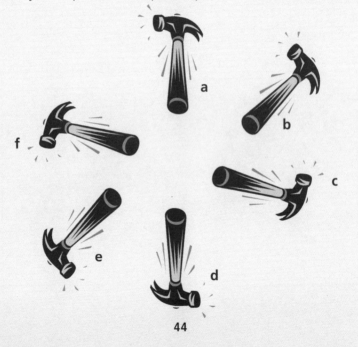

Puzzle 8 OPTICAL CHALLENGE

Are all these white circles the same size? Sometimes it's dangerous to trust your eyes …

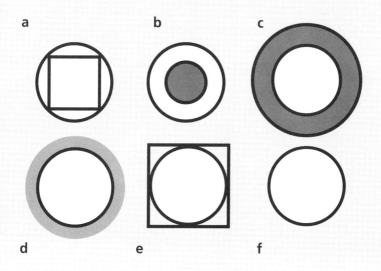

a

b

c

d

e

f

Puzzle 9 CUBISM!

This puzzle really tests your ability to visualize objects in your mind's eye. When the flat shape is folded into a cube, which of the five cubes below does it make?

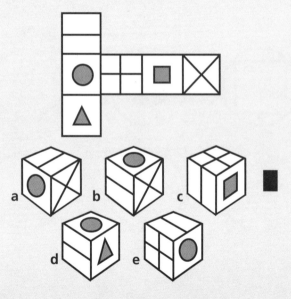

Puzzle 10 DUPLICATE DRAGONS

Only two of the dragons below are identical. Which two?

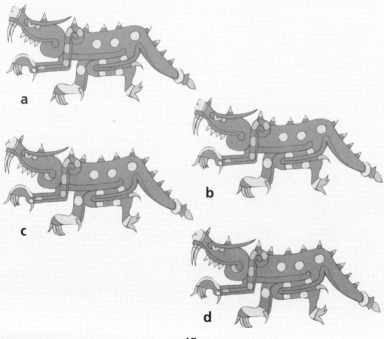

Learning and using language

Employing and playing with language is an essential part of being human. We are the apes who talk. Our world is buzzing with languages. There are 6,912 'living', still-spoken, languages in the world, and a further thousand, such as Latin or Ancient Egyptian, that are known but not in common use.

Experts estimate that there are three million words in the English language, with about two hundred thousand in common use. An educated person probably knows around 10 per cent of these (that is, twenty thousand) and in a typical week would use 1 per cent (around two thousand words). So there is plenty of room to expand your vocabulary!

Words count Confidence with words and good language skills are a key component of almost every part of mental performance. The ability to understand and distinguish precisely between words is essential for logical thinking. The capacity to identify linguistic patterns supports numerical ability and strengthens your memory performance. Being able to conceptualize and express yourself clearly enables you to make the most of your lateral thinking, creative and problem-solving abilities.

Our first words Our ability to understand and make ourselves understood with words is a survival skill we begin to pick up almost as soon as we can breathe. As infants we learn language by imitating others. In experiments with six-month-old babies, researchers could already distinguish between French, Chinese and English babies on the basis of the babbling noise they made. Babies as young as one month old start to distinguish between features of language that they later understand as vowels and consonants.

LEARNING THE LINGO

Educationalists and linguists tell us that adults learn languages in the same way as infants – by mimicry and practice. The best way to learn Spanish, say, is to listen to and talk with Spanish speakers, and to visit Spain or another Spanish-speaking country.

Language and meaning

The body has its own language. You can 'speak' through physical gestures and movements, the expression on your face and body posture. Whether or not you make eye contact, how long you hold it, and how close you stand to someone all convey meaning. In fact, some experts suggest that communication is 90 per cent non-verbal and only 10 per cent words.

Body language can reinforce or undermine a person's words. Business salespeople are trained to be super-vigilant for non-verbal signs that an associate or client is interested, excited or bored by an interaction. Being aware of, reading and then interpreting the body language of people you meet is all part of keeping alert and attentive to mental stimuli – which boosts your brainpower.

If a friend sighs deeply when you are talking to her, you may suspect she is bored or frustrated. If she rolls her eyes or crosses her arms, you would see that she does not believe you and is resisting what you are saying. But what does it mean if she sits on her hands or leans back, at ease, in her chair? Experts would say that these gestures convey that she feels confident and relaxed in your company and that she understands what you are saying without feeling hostile to it. Try watching people more – it is often surprising!

The mother tongue We all need to be surrounded by spoken words in early life. Children who grow up deprived of human company – for example, documented cases of children who were abandoned and raised by wolves in India – cannot speak. In the 7th century BCE the ancient Egyptian pharaoh Psamtek I raised two babies in isolation. He hoped that rather than learn Egyptian from adults they would spontaneously speak an older, 'original' world language. Supposedly their first word sounded like *bekos*, 'bread' in the extinct Phrygian language. Psamtek decided that Phrygian was the world's mother tongue. But more likely, the infants were mimicking the bleating of goats around the shepherd's hut in which they were confined.

Numbers and symbols

Mathematics is an international language par excellence. Because the Arabic numerals 1 to 9 are known around the world, problems of international translation do not affect numbers. Numbers are universal symbols. Having number skills amounts to being fluent in a form of communication that knows no boundaries.

Mathematicians take a playful interest in their subject. Games, puzzles and 'if this, then that' problems have been integral to the progress of the discipline throughout its history.

One of the world's oldest mathematical documents is the Rhind Papyrus, written by a scribe named Ahmes in ancient Egypt in 1850 BCE. In addition to scores of mathematical problems and demonstrations, it contained the following puzzle: 'In seven houses are seven cats. Each cat slays seven mice. Before its death each mouse had consumed seven ears of grain. If permitted to grow, each ear of grain would have produced seven units of wheat. What total do you find?' [Answer: 16,807 units of wheat.]

Another ancient maths brain-tickler is the magic square, a square filled with a sequence of consecutive numbers in such a way that all four sides, all the rows and the two diagonals add up to the same number. The ancient Chinese reputedly developed these tantalizing tricks as early as 2200 BCE. A simple version using the numbers 1–9 is described in the Chinese divination book, the *I Ching*, of c.1150 BCE.

Sudoku The youngest shoot of the mathematical puzzle tree is probably the Sudoku square, or 'number place'. It consists of a nine-squares-by-nine-squares grid containing nine smaller three-by-three grids. Some numbers are included. The player must enter any of the numbers 1–9 so that in the completed grid every line, column and three-by-three grid contains each number only once.

Sudoku was initially developed by retired American architect Howard Garns and first published in *Dell Pencil Puzzles and Word Games* in 1979, before becoming a hit in Japan in 1986 and leaping to international success in 2004–5.

Playing with language

Perhaps because we learn language as infants by mimicking and repeating, playing with words gives us all pleasure from an early age. Take the 'spoonerism', which reverses the initial letters or syllables of two words. Examples include 'wrong load' for 'long road' and a 'lack of pies' for a 'pack of lies'. The man associated with them, the English clergyman William Archibald Spooner, was very nervous in public. He made spoonerisms as slips of the tongue – or 'tips of the slung'.

There are many apocryphal stories of the 'drangers he clopped'. When asking a woman to move to an unoccupied pew in church, he is supposed to have said 'Madam, may I sew you to another sheet?' (rather than 'show you to another seat'). He also reputedly proposed a toast to 'the queer old Dean' rather than the 'dear old Queen'.

The King lives! Another well-loved word game is solving anagrams, which mix up the letters of a word to form another word. The best anagrams cast new light on the idea associated with the original word. Well-known examples include 'flutterby' for 'butterfly', 'dirty room' for 'dormitory' and 'here come dots' for 'the Morse code'. A simple anagram that may give heart to conspiracy theorists who believe that the King of rock'n'roll is still alive is the rearrangement of the letters of 'Elvis' to give you 'lives'.

'Use your loaf' Throughout history people have developed slang and play language – as a game and to exclude others who do not know the 'lingo'. The most celebrated in British English is Cockney rhyming slang, the traditional language of London's Cockneys. Some of the best-loved examples are: 'apples and pears' (stairs), 'Barnet Fair' (hair), 'Cain and Abel' (table), 'jam jar' (car) and 'loaf of bread' (head). These were shortened to make them even harder to understand – as in 'use your loaf', meaning use your head, or think about it.

In addition to solving the language puzzles on the pages that follow, why not try making up your own examples to get you thinking about how to play with language?

Puzzle 11 TONGUE-TWISTING FUN

These tongue-twisters provide a light-hearted linguistic limber-up. Can you help our two protagonists with their teeth-clashingly, tongue-tinglingly troublesome mouthfuls of words?

Sickness at the sheikh's farm

Ayman is a cub reporter sent out to investigate a reported outbreak of disease in farming country owned by a group of sheikhs or village chiefs. He has to report one case of the disease among the chiefs and one among the animals. He gets in a terrible tangle when he tries to phone through to the newsdesk and has to repeat himself eight times over. He says:

'The sixth sick sheikh's sixth sheep's sick. The sixth sick sheikh's sixth sheep's sick. The sixth sick sheikh's sixth sheep's sick. The sixth sick sheikh's sixth sheep's sick. The sixth sick sheikh's sixth sheep's sick. The sixth sick sheikh's sixth sheep's sick. The sixth sick sheikh's sixth sheep's sick. The sixth sick sheikh's sixth sheep's sick.'

The Big Apple

Benedict is extolling the virtues of his city to a guest from out of town. But he's getting carried away as he repeats the reason he loves NY over and over again:

Unique New York, Unique New York, Unique New York, Unique New York, Unique New York, Unique New York.

How many times can you say it before you too need a holiday?

Puzzle 12 CELEBRITY CONFUSION

Test your word power. Each of these anagrams conceals a celebrity. To help you out, we've provided a clue for each.

1 Clue: Rearrange these letters to find a popular US comedian.
Letters: Friendly jeers ....

2 Clue: These letters form the name of which international female singer?
Letters: Her slow cry ....

3 Clue: This is an anagram of the name of which TV talk-show host with a worldwide reputation?
Letters: TV male and tired ....

4 Clue: These letters can be rearranged into the name of an actress who has played a magical character.
Letters: Her hell's real magical ....

Puzzle 13 LANGUAGE BARRIER I

Use your language skills and musical knowledge to uncover the hidden names below.

If Beethoven is QAAKWIBAV,

Tchaikovsky is KDWYEGIBHGU

and Mozart is TIRYZK ...

then who are

QYDW,

QERAK and

QZYWTH?

Puzzle 14 LANGUAGE BARRIER II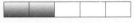
You should be even quicker to solve this word puzzle.

If a Porsche is a CIZHDWA,

a Daimler is a MYETXAZ

and a Renault is a ZAVYOXK …

then what are

a WIVMY, a DEKZIAV

and a XIKOH?

Puzzle 15 STEP BY STEP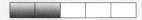

In this number pyramid, every brick is equal to the sum of the two numbers below it. Can you complete the pyramid below? **Hint**: Start at the top and work your way down!

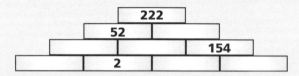

Puzzle 16 CURSE OF THE PHARAOHS

This pyramid is trickier, but if you think carefully about what it's possible to deduce, you should be able to complete it.

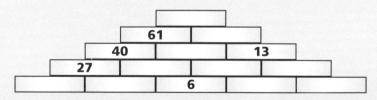

Puzzle 17 WHAT'S NEXT?
At first glance, this may look like a jumble of numbers, but there is a hidden pattern that, if you can uncover it, will help you deduce which number comes next in this numerical sequence.

$$0, \quad 4, \quad 18, \quad 48, \quad 100, \quad ?$$

Puzzle 18 ODD NUMBER OUT
Four of the five numbers below have something in common. A fifth does not. Apply some logical reasoning and some perseverance to work out which is the odd number out?

$$2,358, \quad 45,914, \quad 7,289,$$
$$46,107, \quad 991,810$$

Thinking with emotion

Emotions are a central part of thinking – we can't get rid of them. We have surely all known times when our mental clarity is clouded by jealousy, anger or fear, and we 'can't think straight'. But there are other occasions when we pride ourselves on thinking unemotionally – clearly and logically.

However, we may all be more emotional than we think. Recent scientific research suggests that the ventromedial frontal lobe – one of the parts of the brain believed to govern emotions – is activated when we make seemingly 'rational' decisions for ourselves, such as when to book an appointment with the doctor. Scientists suggest that when a matter affects us personally we 'feel' outcomes in emotional terms and then use the feeling as a guide in deciding.

Behavioural scientists point out that emotions can have a positive impact in enabling us to make quick decisions when under threat. Emotional responses allow us to follow our instincts and act on 'first impressions' – when encountering threatening behaviour on the street, say. But we should also be wary of the emotions because they can inhibit logical and creative thinking, keeping us trapped in an established set of responses and thought patterns, preventing us seeing things from a fresh perspective.

Anatomy of emotion In the brain the amygdala and the hippocampus – elements of the limbic system in the lower brain (*see page 15*) – appear to generate physiological expressions of mood and emotion. Signals from the body received in the frontal lobes of the upper or 'thinking brain' make us aware of emotions. Sometimes stroke victims with damage in the emotional areas of the upper brain experience physiological aspects of an emotion – the quickened heart beat of anger, say – but will not know or feel the emotion.

Emotional intelligence We cannot separate emotions from rational thought. But it helps to be self-aware. 'Emotional intelligence', understanding emotions and how people express them, helps us in interactions with others at work and play.

The power of laughter

Laughter is said to be the 'best medicine'. Doctors tell us laughing is good for our bodily health and helps strengthen our capacity to fight disease by balancing our immune system. We are protected and enlivened by humour.

But humour and laughter are also beneficial for our brain-power and boost our ability to think creatively, to respond flexibly, to deal with change and overcome problems. Humour encourages fresh vision – professional comics often get laughs by looking at everyday things from an unexpected angle.

Laughing is a social activity. Research has shown that people are thirty times more likely to laugh in company than when alone. It strengthens social bonds, helping us relax and seeming to make us trust one another.

Humour and laughter are great stress-busters. Where stress suppresses the immune system, laughter boosts it. And while anxiety can severely reduce your chances of learning something effectively, or working efficiently, a light-hearted approach will relax you and ensure you perform at your best.

When training your memory, adding humorous elements to your memory cues will often make them more effective.

Laughter is as effective as an aerobic workout. A good laugh has so many physiological benefits, such as lowering blood pressure and boosting vascular bloodflow, that scientists believe 100 laughs equals 15 minutes on an exercise bike.

The puzzles and wordplays that follow should tickle your funny bone and raise your awareness of the emotions in thinking. Remember that you will achieve more in your mental life if you can take a sense of fun and a light-hearted perspective into the most serious discussions. The Indian statesman Mahatma Gandhi could often be heard cracking jokes even when he was closeted with political leaders engaged in discussions affecting the very future of his country.

LAUGHTER HEALS
More than a hundred US hospitals have put the healing power of laughter to work by introducing 'laughter rooms' or mobile 'humour carts' stocked with jokebooks, DVDS and comics.

Puzzle 19 SHAPE UP

Use your emotions and have some fun. Which of these shapes and squiggles seems the 'friendliest' to you?

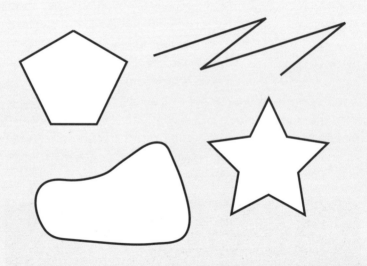

Puzzle 20 NAMING GAME

Here's a simple exercise using your intuition – quickly name each of these mathematical shapes.

Puzzle 21 STARRY EYED

Without using any other equipment, it's possible to see three or more stars on this page. Do you feel challenged by that statement? Do you agree? Using this example, can you learn to seek out loopholes and look at things in different ways?

The memory function

What is the memory? Where is it? If a surgeon cut out part of your brain, could he or she remove all your memories?

Neuroscientists tell us that memory does not reside in a particular part of the brain. They say there is no such thing as a single 'memory mechanism' in the brain. In fact, memory does not exist at all as a concrete, discrete 'thing': it is a way in which the mind works, through a range of complex neurological events that occur throughout the brain.

Mind shrink Some people find their memory begins to fail as they get older. There is some decline in the function of the brain's frontal lobes, which play a key role in managing all brain processes, and this can affect the memory. But otherwise, in the absence of illness or other conditions (*see opposite*), there is no reason why people of a mature age should lose memory function. If they do, it may be because they do not use their mind and the memory enough. The remedy is simple – get thinking, get puzzling, stretch yourself!

Problems such as long-term stress cause memory loss. In part, this is because when you are stressed you cannot concentrate, but there are also physical causes. Prolonged stress appears to release high levels of chemicals called glutamates, which interfere with neuron connections in the hippocampus, one of the memory centres of the brain. Research also shows that medical conditions and hormonal imbalances can inhibit the memory, as for example with changing hormone levels in women during the menopause.

The good news is that even if you do lose memory and other brain functions, they are not lost for ever. In some cases, such as a stroke, permanent damage is caused. But in many others, your brain can recover. You can contribute to the regeneration of your brain by making sure you use it, challenge it and surprise it. Treat it to the unexpected.

> **MEMORY TIP**
> Make sure you are getting enough rest. Research indicates
> that memories are consolidated during sleep.

Short- and long-term memory

You have two types of working memory: short-term and long-term. Short-term memory keeps information for immediate use. Your long-term memory is a store of facts you have memorized, recollections of people, events and so on.

Say you are in a bookshop searching for a book on training the brain, and you ask one of the assistants for advice. After she has looked the information up on her computer she suggests a number of books to consider, including *Brain Book* by Charles Phillips. As you go to the bookshelf to look, you keep the information in your short-term memory. If the book is not there and you decide to buy it elsewhere, you will have to memorize the details – and transfer the information to your long-term memory. If it is there, but you decide not to buy it, you will probably discard the information altogether. It drops out of your short-term memory, never to be seen again!

The brain revolution If you are a reader of mature years who feels that you cannot remember as well as you once did, you may have an unconscious mental image of the memory as a filing cabinet or computer disk and be wondering if after many years of learning and remembering your storage unit is too full to contain any more. As we have seen, the exciting news of the 'brain revolution' is that we use only one tiny part of our brain's abilities. Your memory can never be full. Its capacity for storing information is almost limitless. There are many fun techniques for improving how you learn and store information and your methods of recall. Just read on!

Eat yourself brainy Foods rich in saturated fats – such as potato chips, burgers and French fries, and processed snack foods – may have a negative effect on the memory because they appear to reduce levels of BDNF (brain-derived neurotrophic factor), a chemical in the brain good for growth of neurons and consolidation of connections between them. Fresh and canned fish, brightly coloured vegetables and fruit – such as salad leaves, blackberries, raspberries and so on – have a positive effect, because they energize brain cells.

How we remember

Some things are easier to remember than others. For one thing, it's no problem to store and retrieve information that interests you. If you like cinema, you will find it easier to remember the films of Steven Spielberg or the Coen brothers than to learn and recall something that leaves you cold – the names of flowers, say. You pay more attention to information that engages you. Your brain is 'switched on' by attention chemicals, both when storing and retrieving information.

Concrete sticks We generally remember concrete things better than abstract ideas, so casting an abstract idea in the form of a concrete, 3D image makes it easier to remember. We recall the bizarre more readily than the run-of-the-mill, so try to create a bizarre image and link it with a fact you are learning. Many people benefit from visualizing what they are trying to learn, others prefer verbal or numerical patterns.

When we come to the brain-training section, we will learn that neuroscientists and memory experts recommend that you process information in as many ways as possible when learning it. By doing this you involve several areas and systems of the brain – tying in visual, smell or hearing systems as well as linguistic ones. The more neural connections you make, the simpler your brain will find it to recall the information.

Mnemonics An example is learning the names of the notes on a musical stave. In the bass clef, used for writing lower notes, the spaces between the lines represent the notes A,C, E and G. A mnemonic to help you remember is All Cows Eat Grass. It also helps to visualize cows eating grass, and perhaps imagine the sound of the bells chiming the notes A, C, E and G as they do so. Process the information in as many other ways as you can. For example, think of four friends – Alfie, Charlie, Erica and Gemma – and fix their faces in your mind.

KNOW YOURSELF
Know yourself and play to your strengths. If you are stronger on the visual than the verbal, cast your information in visual terms.

Memory-training regime

Training the memory involves trying out the many memory techniques detailed in this section and on pages 168–86 and discovering which work best for you. Experiment with using visualization, memorable phrases, musical cues, links to your feelings and so on. Once you have done this, you will benefit from a little planning. Choose which areas of your memory you'd like to improve first – perhaps your ability to remember names and faces in social situations, your capacity for remembering facts for quizzes, or your 'running memory' that enables you to keep track of your car keys and your wallet.

Devise a strategy for enhancing your chosen memory function, and set yourself achievable and measurable targets to help chart your progress. For example, if you decide to work on your memory for faces and names, choose a technique such as linking names to visualized objects associated with the name or the person's appearance. Set yourself targets to improve and be sure to check whether you have reached them.

A key part of memory-training regimes is self-testing. Revisit what you have learnt and try to recall it. Do this at increasing intervals: for example, at thirty seconds, five minutes, one hour, six hours, one day, one week later. Self-testing is crucial: reviewing the information reinforces the neural connections made when learning for the first time.

The power of attention To get the most from your memory, pay active attention both when inputting material to your brain (when reading, for example) and when recalling the information. It is advisable to practise doing one thing at a time. It's harder than it sounds. But it trains the attention and develops your powers of concentration. When you are reading, don't listen to the TV in the background. When talking to your daughter, give her your full attention – do not let your mind run on to planning your next day's work.

Try the puzzles that follow: as well as training the brain's memory systems, they provide a lively workout for your powers of observation, information storage, and recall.

Puzzle 22 SHAPELY FUN

Study the shapes below for one minute (get someone to time you if you can). Then turn to page 78 to see how many of the questions you're able to answer. Is your memory as good as you thought it was? If not, try the puzzle again once you've tried out some brain-training, to see if you've improved.

Puzzle 23 A TALL STORY

Have you got a memory for facts? If you have, you'll find this memory test no problem. Read the text below twice only, then attempt the questions on page 79.

Three fishermen sit patiently by the banks of the River Phew, close to the main road to Huntington, a small town to the west of New Barney, just before East Boulder. Chuck, Henry and Ivan, a father, son and grandfather respectively, are not known for their fishing prowess. Their wives are not expecting fish for dinner. Last time, on 8 October, they returned with nothing more than a cold after 4 hours and 20 minutes. This time, things seem more hopeful. After 18 minutes Chuck gets a bite, but it's just an old tyre. Seven minutes later, Henry senses some motion, but it's just a bird. After another 43 minutes, a noise startles them. The son reacts first. 'Bear,' he whispers. The three men stand still. Downstream, to their right, stands a bear, a huge fish, nearly 2 ft long, in its mouth. Suddenly a jet roars by and the bear runs off. But not before it drops the fish. The three men return home, for once triumphant.

Puzzle 22 SHAPELY FUN QUESTIONS

Well, can you answer all of these questions without the need to look back?

1 How many shapes are there in total? ....

2 How many circles are there? ....

3 If we number the columns 1–4, in which column does an upside-down triangle appear? ....

4 Which is the only column that has a circle at the bottom? ....

5 Which is the only column of the four to have a diamond in it? ....

6 Can you remember the middle shape in the first column? ....

7 How many triangles are there altogether? ....

8 Which shapes make up the second column? ....

9 In which column does a square sit between two triangles? ....

10 What is the top right shape? ....

Puzzle 23 A TALL STORY QUESTIONS
Did you take the bait? Can you tackle the questions
below?

1 What is the name of the river that appears in this
tall story?...

2 What is the last town mentioned? ....

3 Name the three men. ....

4 Can you remember which one of the three is
the father? ....

5 Give the date of their last trip. ....

6 Who is the unfortunate fisherman who catches
an old tyre? ....

7 After how many minutes does a bird appear in
the story? ....

8 Does the bear appear to the left or the right of
the men? ....

9 Who hears the bear? ....

10 How big is the fish the men 'catch'? ....

Puzzle 24 WING IT!

Admire this butterfly for just a minute, then see if you can answer the questions on page 82.

Puzzle 25 ROAD SIGN RECALL

Look closely at these road signs for a minute then try to answer the questions on page 83 without getting your brain into gridlock.

40

6

67

5

120

24

8

71

12

Puzzle 24 WING IT! QUESTIONS

Can you answer these questions about the image on page 80 without looking back?

1 Do the butterfly's antennae curl outwards or inwards? ....

2 How many segments is the main body made from? ....

3 On the lower wings, do the circles get bigger or smaller as you move up? ....

4 And how many circles are on each lower wing? ....

5 How many dashes is the parallel line on each top wing broken into? ....

6 How many uninterrupted parallel lines are there on each top wing? ....

7 Are the eyes circular or oval? ....

8 Is the butterfly exactly symmetrical? ....

9 How many circles are there altogether on the wings? ....

10 Is the butterfly's tail tip rounded or pointed? ....

Puzzle 25 ROAD SIGN RECALL QUESTIONS

And can you answer these questions about the road signs on page 81 without looking back?

1 How many signs have an outer white rim? ....

2 How many of the road signs are a multiple of 6? ....

3 What's the sum of the top row? ....

4 How many odd numbers are there in total? ....

5 If you multiply the bottom left by the middle left figure does it equal the top left total? ....

6 How many of the signs show numbers greater than 50? ....

7 How many times does the number 1 appear? ....

8 What's the total of the two signs in the bottom row without a white rim? ....

9 How many numbers are less than 10? ....

10 What's the biggest number and where does it appear? ....

The puzzler's repertoire of skills

Your friend has a jigsaw puzzle but the box is missing, so she doesn't have a reproduction of the picture she's trying to recreate. She's asked you to help her begin – what skills do you use? To start with, you would probably use logic and a knowledge of how jigsaws work to identify and connect the outer pieces.

Now you have a 'frame' for the puzzle, you may begin to arrange the other pieces in clusters of similar colours. Intuition may give you a lead, suggesting that the white pieces form a cloud and should be high on the image. If you have good visual skills and can recognize and remember patterns, this will help you fit individual pieces and larger segments together. You will also need patience – and lots of it!

The clear-thinking, logic, intuition and visual ability required for the jigsaw are among the key skills needed for puzzle-solving. To unpick and rebuild the wooden cube puzzle with this book, for example, you'll need to practise strong visual–spatial sense – the ability to think in three dimensions.

Other forms of puzzling, such as the crossword, demand a wide vocabulary and word-handling skills. The anagram and similar word games also call for the capacity to see and handle patterns in language. Quizzes require good powers of memory – as well as a decent general knowledge. Others, such as maths teasers and Sudoku grids, need an ability to juggle numbers.

Another mental skill that's a must for the puzzler is lateral thinking. This requires the capacity to make unexpected connections, to rethink problems and see them from a fresh perspective, to ignore conventional boundaries.

Learn and expand The good news is that all these skills can be developed and perfected with use. You probably don't yet feel like an expert puzzler in all these areas, but you can be – with practice. The even better news is that practice is good fun! I'm not asking you to put in hours of learning by rote or fitness training. Just take this book, open the 'mental skills box' in your brain, and start using your puzzle tools.

What is logic?

In the modern, media-saturated world – where we are bombarded with facts, arguments and statements purporting to be truth – we are well-advised to maintain a healthy level of scepticism as we attempt to see beyond appearances. We can all benefit from techniques, such as logical analysis, that help preserve clarity and independence of mind.

An understanding of logic enables us to distinguish between well-reasoned and badly reasoned arguments. Logical analysis is an algebra of reason, used to examine and unpick the links in a chain of argument.

Logical basis In a logical argument, the sequence of reasoning is sound – so if the starting point is true, then the conclusion must be true. But in an illogical argument, with a false chain of reasoning, even if the initial facts are true the conclusion will be false. Because they are apparently based on true facts, some illogical arguments are extremely beguiling – at first sight you often think 'that must be correct'.

An example of a logical argument is the following: all Xs are Y; all Ys are Z; therefore all Xs are Z – 'All children are human beings; all human beings are mammals; therefore all children are mammals.' But an example of an argument that sometimes seems logical at first sight is the structure: all Ys are Z; X is a Z; therefore X is a Y – 'All human beings are mammals; the African elephant is a mammal; therefore the African elephant is a human being.'

Our example is obviously false, but many arguments of this type in religion or politics are less easy to spot. It greatly helps our thinking if we can recognize and label illogical thinking in action.

Spot the flaws If you want to raise your awareness of logical processes, train yourself to look for logical flaws in arguments from politicians or 'experts' on TV and radio. Buy newspapers or magazines from differing political or philosophical camps to check how journalists and copy editors slant identical facts to make contrasting news stories.

Logical thinking

A spy followed top-secret instructions: 'Go to shoe shop A, turn left and walk 200 paces, turn right and walk 100 paces, cross road to meeting point B (a park bench) to meet agent X.' But he started from the wrong shoe shop and therefore, although he followed the instructions with the utmost care, he could not find the park bench or agent X.

When we are thinking, the most flawless logic will lead to the wrong conclusion if we start from a mistaken assumption. Equally, the integrity of logical arguments depends on the beginning statement being true – if the initial premise is false then the whole structure collapses. Consider this example: 'All children are truthful; Jim is a child; therefore Jim never lies.' This is logically impeccable, but probably inaccurate because the initial premise is highly questionable.

Logic and creative insight The creative logician Arthur Conan Doyle's fictional detective Sherlock Holmes is revered as the master of logical thought. Sherlock loved to stress the ease with which he had solved problems that had defeated others – given the clues, the solution was 'elementary'. In fact 'Holmesian' detective work usually combined acute observation and creative insight with logical inference. Sherlock's ability to notice details that others had overlooked was at least as important as his powers of logical thought.

Once he had gathered the evidence, he was adept at marshalling and interpreting it. He used logic to arrange facts and then make connections that had not occurred to other people. Sherlock declared in the story *The Sign of Four*, 'How often have I said to you that when you have eliminated the impossible, whatever remains, however improbable, must be the truth?' Curiously, the 'logical' Sherlock in fact thrived on being able to think creatively, to see arrangements that others discounted because they were improbable.

In our thinking, logic is a tool rather than an end in itself. We cannot rely entirely on logic. Sherlock Holmes and other great thinkers combined foolproof logic with the ability to make unexpected leaps of connection.

Everyday uses for logical thinking

In day-to-day life, we talk about 'doing detective work', or being a 'Sherlock'. We often have to search out the information we need to make a decision, or painstakingly go through possible permutations to find the cause of a problem.

Computer-users may need all their reserves of logical analysis to work out why a particular file always crashes their machine. DIY aficionados are familiar with the process of gradually eliminating potential causes of a problem – such as why the bedroom light switch keeps tripping the fuse. Car mechanics are used to going through possible causes, and chains of causes, when finding out why the engine won't start, say, or why it keeps stalling.

In general thinking, too, everyone can benefit from using step-by-step logical analysis to check our decisions. As we have seen on earlier pages, emotions play an important role in our thinking processes – both in terms of 'colouring' our perceptions of facts and creating strong attachments to particular conclusions.

We may want very much to reach a particular conclusion – so much so, that we convince ourselves that something is in our interest when it is not.

Christmas lights logic If you have a string of lights on your Christmas tree, you'll find as often as not that the lights do not work when you turn them on. Because a single broken bulb or wayward wire breaks the chain of connections, if there is one problem none of the lights work. You have to go through the lights one by one until you find the culprit.

If we check our thinking like a string of lights, checking the stages one at a time, we should be able to identify our emotional bias and adjust the decision accordingly. We can ask, 'Is that initial premise accurate?', 'Do the stages in the argument proceed rationally?', 'Am I guilty of fudging one part of the argument so I can reach the conclusion I want?'

The exercises on the pages that follow use patterns of symbols and codes to exercise and strengthen your powers of logical thought, deduction and creative solution.

Puzzle 26 LOGIC AND SYMBOLS

These symbols represent the numbers 1 to 4. If each aeroplane represents the number 3, logical reasoning should enable you to work out the values of all the symbols so the sum adds up.

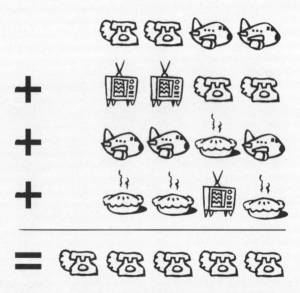

92

Puzzle 27 SYMBOLS MAZE

Starting in the middle of the grid, use your logic to work out how best to visit each square in turn. Which is the last square visited?

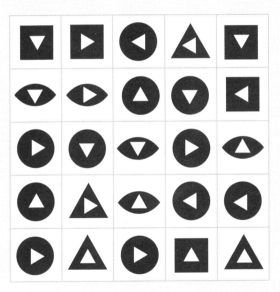

Puzzle 28 NUMBER JIG AROUND

Now's your chance to combine number skills and logic. Can you fit these numbers into the grid? Be warned: there is only one solution, so if you put the wrong number in the wrong place you may have to start again. One number has already been placed to get you started.

3 Digits
263
358
413
517
~~629~~
972

4 Digits
1930
2947
3226
4765
5821
6569
7346
9411

5 Digits
17981
21837
36289
48914
54761
68368
71780
76224
81056
91510

6 Digits
124141
417972
612616
869149

7 Digits
1973862
2685774
2783438
3276241
3611529
4249792
4559703
5844343
6345105
6979614
7693496
8240115
8334849
9763350

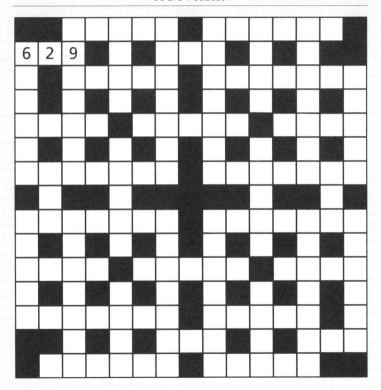

Puzzle 29 SHOP TILL YOU DROP

Five women set off for the annual sales – all ready to do battle for a bargain! Each woman bought a blouse, a skirt, and a hat of a different colour. Using the grid opposite and the clues below, can you work out who bought what? **Hint**: Look back to page 35 for some logical tips.

1 The blouse bought by the woman who also bought an orange hat is of a different colour from the skirt bought by Karen, whose hat is blue.

2 Phylis bought a red skirt. Karen is neither the woman who bought a green skirt nor the one who bought the red blouse.

3 The woman who bought a brown blouse bought a skirt of a different colour from the blouse bought by Rose, who bought a brown hat.

4 Sue bought a green blouse and a skirt of the same colour as the hat bought by Patty.

		BLOUSE					HAT					SKIRT				
		BLUE	BROWN	GREEN	ORANGE	RED	BLUE	BROWN	GREEN	ORANGE	RED	BLUE	BROWN	GREEN	ORANGE	RED
SHOPPER	KAREN															
	PATTY															
	PHYLIS															
	ROSE															
	SUE															
SKIRT	BLUE															
	BROWN															
	GREEN															
	ORANGE															
	RED															
HAT	BLUE															
	BROWN															
	GREEN															
	ORANGE															
	RED															

What is lateral thinking?

The psychologist Edward de Bono invented the concept of 'lateral thinking' in 1967. He proposed a mental strategy in which we try to think beyond given perceptions, concepts and boundaries. Using the example of chess, he suggested that traditional thinking is playing chess with the normal pieces to conventional rules, but lateral thinking might involve adding squares to the board, using different pieces or moving them in new, previously unaccepted ways.

Future thinking Another example de Bono gives is that of digging a hole. Traditional thinking is digging the hole deeper, and experimenting with various tools and methods to dig. But lateral thinking – which he sometimes calls 'future thinking' because he believes we need to adopt it to facilitate future progress – might involve digging another quite different hole in a new place. He declares: 'Traditional thinking is all about "what is"; Future thinking will also need to be about "what can be".'

A powerful example of lateral thinking in practice is the clockwork radio developed by British inventor Trevor Bayliss. He was inspired to develop the radio by a TV programme that described the need to spread public health information in an Africa ravaged by AIDS, but added that in many areas electricity supplies were uncertain and people could not afford batteries. He made the lateral leap of considering 'what if?' What if we used people as a source of energy? What if we made a radio that could be powered by hand? He developed the Freeplay hand-cranked radio that runs on springpower. It won the 1996 BBC Design Award for Best Product and Best Design and the following year Bayliss was awarded the OBE.

Another practical application of lateral thinking is the Pompidou Centre in Paris. Architects Richard Rogers and Renzo Piano made the lateral leap of considering what if the elevator, lift shaft and essential piping were on the outside rather than the inside of the building? This freed up room for large exhibition spaces within the centre. It became one of the most visited and talked-about buildings in Europe.

Children and lateral thinking

'Why do you do it like that?', 'Why can't you do it like this?', 'What if you tried doing this instead?', 'Why are we doing this rather than that?' These kinds of questions – often asked by children – can be very difficult to answer. Sometimes you are reduced to saying 'Because we've always done it like that', 'When you grow up, you'll learn that everybody does it like that,' etc.

Children's natural inquisitiveness and willingness to range beyond conventional boundaries allow them to engage naturally in what lateral thinking pioneer Edward de Bono calls 'creative thinking'. By contrast, adults and educators are stuck in 'critical thinking', in an obsession with knowledge. Where adults consider only 'what is', lateral-thinking youngsters consider 'what may be' and 'what can be'.

De Bono forcefully expresses a concern that our education system stifles this lateral-thinking and creative impulse in our children. We load them with vast numbers of facts. But we do not teach them how to think. In the end we seek to turn the young into versions of ourselves – wedded to tradition and adversarial methods of argument, distrustful of creativity and cooperative debate.

Yet we have plenty to learn from the uninhibited, unfettered thinking of the young. One area that de Bono himself highlights is addressing large, seemingly impossible problems such as poverty or pollution. We are obsessed, he suggests, with 'what is', with removing the causes of problems. We should endeavour to free ourselves to look forward by considering 'what can be'. Forget removing the cause, and concentrate on the important part – finding a solution.

Accentuate the impossible One reason the young – and the young-at-mind – prove good at lateral thinking is that they are unaware of or dismissive of constraints, of what is possible or impossible. We can learn from this by considering solutions that at first sight seem impossible. Consider the elements of the problem, then attempt something different by breaking them apart to recombine them in a fresh and unexpected way.

Everyday lateral thinking

Every time we have a problem that has no clear solution we have the chance to practise creative lateral thinking. The solutions we come up with are usually so obvious that we groan inwardly as we think, 'I can't believe I couldn't see it before'.

A sticky problem A couple of years ago, when I was working in a publishing company's office, I was typing normally on my computer when suddenly all the words on the screen highlighted themselves and then deleted themselves. The same thing happened several times, and in some agitation I called the company's computer technician to help. He tried reloading the word-processing program I was using, then reloaded the computer's system. I sat twiddling my thumbs. Finally he was called away.

Later a second technician came – and he must have had a gift for lateral thinking, for he saw at once what the problem was. My keyboard was sticky (I remembered then that I had spilled a tiny splash of fruit juice on it). The command key was sticking down after I pressed it, so that when I carried on typing I inadvertently ordered the computer to highlight all the text and then to delete it all! He replaced the keyboard. Everything was as it had been before the problem arose, except that my respect for lateral thinking had grown.

Each day we encounter problems that could be solved by lateral thinking. How do you prevent the TV remote control going missing all the time? How do you stop yourself losing your car keys? How can you go to the gym, go shopping, have lunch and phone home during your lunch-hour?

The exercises on the following pages will stretch your mind as they explore your capacity to question assumptions, ask key questions, make creative combinations and think through all solutions – be sure to consider even the 'impossible' ones. Try the exercises for a brisk mental workout, then afterwards endeavour to carry the techniques with you into daily life and to use them when dealing with both major and minor difficulties.

Puzzle 30 NOTHING ON EARTH
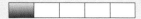

Use your powers of lateral thinking to explain why what looks like a pile of rubbish used to amount to something …

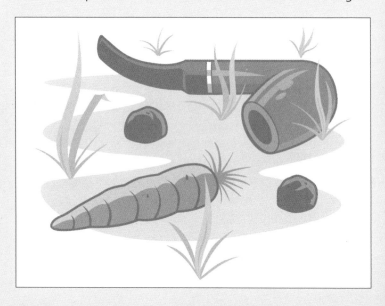

Puzzle 31 CAN YOU CANOE?
The answer to this lateral conundrum may come to you if you can think outside the box …

A tourist canoeing in her own boat on a lake came across three boys arguing on the shore by a flotilla of rental canoes, similar to her own. She stopped to ask the reason for the debate. It transpired that the boys' father had left them in charge of the business for a week, and that the eldest lad would look after half the boats, the middle child a third of the flotilla, and the youngest an eighth. Each boy was to keep the revenue from his rentals. The company owned 23 canoes. How did the passing paddler manage to solve the sons' dispute to everyone's satisfaction, without using a saw?

Puzzle 32 CAKE RING MYSTERY
Can you solve this mystery using a bit of lateral know-how?

A cake-maker is baking a consignment of walnut cakes for delivery to her local shop. When all eleven cakes are finished, she discovers to her horror that her gold wedding ring is missing and that she must have baked it into a cake! After a think, she realizes that the cake containing the ring will be heavier than the others, and resolves to use her scales to find the ring. The shop shuts in ten minutes. Can you describe how, in a maximum of three weighs, she can find out which cake contains her ring, without destroying the whole consignment?

Puzzle 33 JOLLY ODD SHAPES

These little droodles below are all depicting something. Can you work out what by tapping into your powers of lateral thinking?

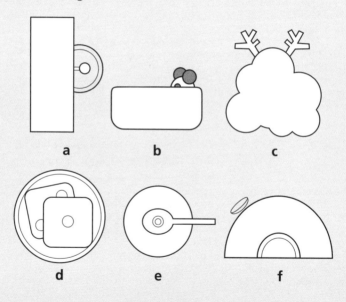

a   b   c

d   e   f

Puzzle 34 LATERAL ARCHITECT

Assuming all the blocks on the unseen sides of this pile are present, how many small cubes must be added to make a large cube measuring 4 x 4? Unleash your powers of imagination to get to the bottom of the problem.

Intuition and problem-solving

Sometimes we know the answer to a problem without understanding how we reached the solution. We say we know by intuition or that we 'trusted our instinct'.

Intuition can produce a leap of imagination that delivers a fresh perspective on a problem. Or it can bring a moment of quiet insight that seems like good old common sense.

The words 'intuition' and 'instinct' are often used as if interchangeable. But at other times they have different meanings, and it helps clarity to distinguish between them.

'Instinct' sometimes means a primal response – like the 'fight or flight' instinct triggered when we feel we are in danger. Hormones pumping, we prepare to run or turn to defend ourselves. In these cases, instinct does not involve thought, and appears to derive principally from areas of the lower brain that generate the physiological elements of emotion.

But intuition is a higher-brain process. In following your intuition, you use subconscious memory and knowledge of previous outcomes. You may subconsciously be using your understanding to sift through patterns or other information you have noticed without being aware you were noticing it.

Have a break Intuition appears to work best when we are not busy with conscious thought. If you are stuck with a problem, the best way to bring intuition to bear is to take a break. Make a cup of tea, go for a run or a workout, have a nap, listen to some music or play the piano. When you return you may find that the answer appears quickly.

Having a nap is a good idea because sleep appears to be particularly effective in releasing intuitive energy. If you have time, come back to the problem in the morning. The history of science and invention is full of tales of pioneers who returned refreshed from their dreams to find solutions. American engineer Elias Howe, for example, hit on the design for his lock-stitch sewing machine after he dreamt he was being attacked by spear-wielding tribesmen. It gave him the intuitive insight that he should use a needle with a hole in the tip rather than in the middle for his design!

Can you identify one person among your family or friends who is the most intuitive? If you can, is that person male or female? Is he or she young, middle-aged, more mature? It may be that younger people, who generally are less constrained by traditional categories in their thinking, are freer than others to experiment with intuition. Perhaps mature people, who have a wealth of experience, apply their knowledge of life by finding intuitive responses to problems.

British prime minister Stanley Baldwin declared, 'I would rather trust a woman's instinct than a man's reason'. There is a general 'common sense' view that women are the more intuitive. Baldwin, who died in 1947, knew a world in which far fewer women worked. Men were more likely to be schooled in official or corporate thinking, and women were freer to think intuitively. Yet many would say that his words capture a general truth – that women give intuition a freer rein.

Developing intuition In truth we all have the capacity to be powerfully intuitive. As with the other kinds of 'brainpower', in the area of intuition we have great abilities of which we may be unaware or simply not bother to use. We can develop our intuition.

When you're considering problems at work or home, or when you're relaxing with puzzles or a game, be open to your intuitive insights. You may have developed a habit of brushing them aside. Listen to and value your intuition and your awareness of it will develop. The more you use and trust it, the better your intuition will function.

For although it may seem a mysterious quality, intuition is a capacity we can develop through practice. To some extent our ability to be intuitive depends on 'local knowledge'. You're better able to intuit the feelings and responses of people you know well because you're familiar with how they show their emotions. And you're more likely to intuit the solution to a problem or a puzzle you're familiar with.

Use the puzzles on the pages that follow to test your powers of perception, to learn about your instincts and to exercise your developing intuition.

Puzzle 35 VISION & INTUITION
How many shapes are in this diagram? Take an intuitive guess. How could you improve your technique next time?

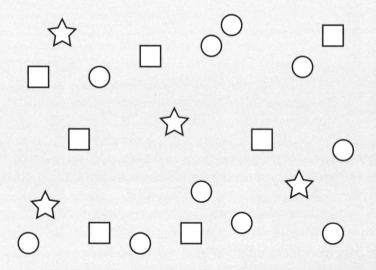

112

Puzzle 36 INTERSECT

How many line intersections are there in this diagram? Again, take an intuitive guess. Can you think of ways to do better next time you try it?

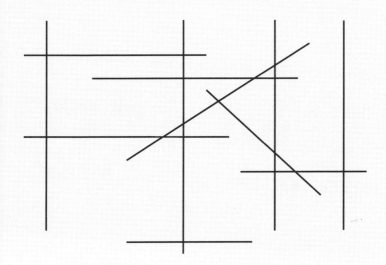

Puzzle 37 SUM IT UP

Test your numerical intuition. For each row, guess the total intuitively. Don't think about any one row for more than three seconds. How close can you get to the correct answer?

a	8	1	4	7	
b	9	5	7	8	
c	11	19	4	13	
d	8	6	7	2	11
e	18	10	1	14	12
f	30	91	48	20	55

Puzzle 38 Z TO A

For each row, state whether none, one or two items are out of alphabetical order. Don't think about any one row for more than three seconds. How many did you get right?

a	A	H	K	J	L
b	AR	BM	BO	CP	CQ
c	Car	Cat	Cut	Cot	Cop
d	Farm	Form	Fort	Four	Fuse
e	Greed	Green	Greet	Great	Groat
f	Parcel	Parsley	Penny	Pencil	Pocket

BRAIN TRAINING

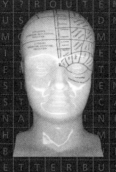

In this section you'll find detailed guidance on how to train your brain. This workshop combines clear explanatory text with practice exercises to stretch your visual–spatial skills, your ability with language and numbers, and your creative-thinking powers, as well as strengthening your memory and powers of recall.

Exercising the brain

Sometimes – on vacation, perhaps – you attempt a physical activity such as horse-riding or volleyball that you don't usually try. The next day you have aches in places you didn't know existed. You have worked muscles that normally remain unexercised.

Brain training is like the kind of physical workout that exercises muscles you're not accustomed to using. But after brain training, instead of waking up with aches and pains, you find you have a slightly sharper thinking power, a greater alertness, and the beginnings of a fresh mental energy.

The key aspect of brain training is to accustom your brain to new activities. As we have seen in the first part of the book, when you attempt something different you make new connections between brain cells. This boosts your overall brain performance and increases your working intelligence.

So avoid routine – in your life, your leisure pursuits and your puzzling. As I have advised before, do things you don't normally do, attempt puzzles you don't normally attempt.

Seek out novelty in your mental life. Skip lunch and visit an art gallery. Experiment with listening to a new type of music – classical, rock, jazz. Visit an area of the bookstore you don't normally visit. Read a genre of fiction you have never before sampled – how about science fiction or historical romance? Watch a new TV show. Take up a completely new pastime, such as playing your son at his computer games.

Changes like these keep you attentive to experience – and as we have seen when you are attentive, you strengthen the brain by releasing neuromodulators (chemicals that bolster brain-cell connections).

Resist habits In everyday life, why not make small, deliberate changes to your routine? Walk a short journey – to work, church or the cinema – that you normally drive. Go to bed an hour later or earlier. Visit a different sandwich shop. Taste a food you've never eaten before. Change your image. Try a new colour or hairstyle. Whatever happens, endeavour to keep up your levels of curiosity about the world around you.

The benefits of brain training

There are bonuses for everyone in training the brain. A regular mental 'workout' keeps the brain firing, forging and consolidating pathways among its millions of neurons. This safeguards mental performance and helps to prevent the effects of ageing on thinking and memory. Older folk can prevent or even reverse mental decline through daily exercises that increase bloodflow to the brain.

Over-50s with demanding jobs that set them new challenges are less likely to suffer memory loss and other types of mental decline, because their brains are continually stretched. But you can achieve the same effect by making sure you challenge yourself. Keep learning. Your brain will never be 'full'. It has the capacity to store a thousand pieces of information every second of your life – from babyhood to old age. That's 86,400 thousand a day, 604,800 thousand a week.

Learning a language is one of the best forms of mental exercise you can choose. Scientists have discovered that people who are bilingual maintain higher levels of activity than normal in the brain's frontal lobes. As we grow older, the frontal lobes can be vulnerable to the effects of ageing, but bilingual people may suffer no such mental dulling.

The power of concentration Brain training can have powerful results. Concentration exercises such as meditation can train our powers of attention sufficiently to override inbuilt physiological and mental mechanisms. Normally when your two eyes are presented with different images, the brain is wired to fluctuate between them – a process called 'perceptual rivalry'. But a research programme in 2005 showed that Buddhist monks, who have harnessed their attention through meditation, could override this innate impulse and concentrate fully on only one of the two images.

Or if meditation's not your thing, why not take up an instrument? Research at the University of California with young children found that those who played and sung music daily were 80 per cent better at problem-solving tests than those who took no part in musical performances.

Keep trying

Don't be put off if you find some puzzles very difficult to solve. Perhaps you feel you are no good at maths or at visual–spatial tests. Don't give up. Don't avoid these kinds of tests.

Brain research indicates that you give your brain the best workout if you offer it varied tests – and if you stretch it by testing it in the most challenging ways. Just as when you are getting fit, the muscles most in need of strengthening are the ones you don't normally use, so the areas of your brain that need the most exercise are the ones you avoid exercising.

Remember that facing up to and overcoming challenges will bring you a great sense of satisfaction and lift your spirits. It will release mood-boosting chemicals into your brain (*see pages 20–1*).

If necessary, look up the answer to puzzles you can't do. Don't think of it as cheating – you're learning something valuable that will help you tackle other puzzles. So use it as a way of spurring yourself on. Find the answer, then attempt to redo the puzzle and others like it, and work out *how* it was done.

Get 'in the zone' When top athletes are competing at the peak of their game, they are totally involved in every aspect. Commentators say that athletes like these are 'in the zone'.

If you improve your mental agility, levels of alertness and powers of concentration through the exercises in this book, you can find your own way to be 'in the zone', both when doing puzzles and in your everyday life. (A simple mental exercise to begin training is suggested on page 123.)

Top athletes also work very hard to identify and improve the weak points of their game. We can learn from this, too. As you go through the book's different brainpower sections and exercises, you'll become aware of your weaker areas. If you find visual–spatial puzzles hardest, concentrate your efforts on these. If you're struggling with your memory, use our tests and games to improve your memory performance.

AN OPEN MIND
Try to keep an open mind. Seeing things from unfamiliar angles and new perspectives improves your mental agility.

Your brain-training regime

You probably set aside a regular time for keeping fit – through a trip to the gym, a brisk walk or some gardening. Why not make a particular effort to keep your brain fit too?

Set aside 10–15 minutes each day or a half-hour every other day. Use the exercises provided in this part of the book for a regular mental workout. If you commute by train or bus, or if you walk to work, you could do your 'brain gym' to keep your neurons firing while travelling.

Complete the exercises in a concentrated, dedicated way. Test yourself and record your progress. Note how long it takes you to do a particular type of test and again when you next try a similar puzzle – compare your score to see if you have improved. You'll probably find that 'practice makes perfect', and that perseverance brings surprising breakthroughs.

The concentrated mind I recommend trying a 'concentration workout', too. Most of us are guilty of dissipating our mental powers because we are unable really to concentrate. We may settle down to work on a crossword, say, but within a minute we are thinking about what to buy someone for Christmas.

By contrast, most if not all of the great thinkers, artists and scientists have shared one thing above all others – the capacity for single-minded pursuit of their goal and for really powerful concentration. This is one reason why we have the affectionate caricature of the 'absent-minded professor', who is a brilliant neuroscientist, say, but cannot be trusted to choose matching socks in the morning.

To start training your concentration, use a simple meditation exercise such as 'counting the breath'. Sit upright in a straight-backed chair, comfortable but not slumping. Close your eyes and lay your hands in your lap. Concentrate on your breathing and count the breaths in and out, up to ten. Breathe steadily, but don't breathe especially deeply. When you reach ten begin again from one. You'll probably find that your mind wanders: each time bring it calmly back to your breathing and counting. Try to do this for 10–20 minutes a day and you'll find your powers of concentration improve.

The cross-wired brain

As we have seen (*page 15*), the upper brain is divided into two parts, the left and right hemispheres. The left hemisphere controls the right side of the body and the right hemisphere commands the left side. This becomes apparent when something goes wrong with the arrangement – a stroke that causes damage to the right side of the brain, for example, can result in paralysis on the body's left side.

In addition, research has indicated that each side has specialized functions. One side or the other takes the dominant role in particular mental activities.

In San Francisco, California, Professor Robert Ornstein monitored brain activity in experimental subjects who were performing contrasting activities – first, doing maths and, second, matching coloured patterns. Ornstein measured the subjects' brainwaves (*see page 17*), in particular the alpha waves (9 to 14 cycles per second) that indicate a relaxed mental state. When working on maths, the subjects showed increased alpha waves in the right as compared to the left hemisphere, suggesting that the left hemisphere was more active and the right at rest. When matching colours, on the other hand, the subjects' alpha waves indicated that they were more active in the right, more relaxed in the left hemisphere.

The two hemispheres Awareness of specialization led some theorists to envisage the hemispheres as two parallel brains, the 'left brain' and the 'right brain'. Such analysis of mental performance suggests that the left brain takes a dominant role in rational and analytical thought, while the right brain specializes in creative thinking and visual–spatial perception.

Left-brain specialities are largely verbal and numerical. They include logic, maths, analysis, linear sequences, reading, writing, and language use. The left brain appears to dominate when information is processed sequentially – that is, one piece after another, as in writing or reading. The right brain, by contrast, dominates when we process several things simultaneously – for example, when we see eyes, nose, ears, cheeks, chin and recognize them as a familiar face.

The right brain

The right hemisphere plays a dominant role in essentially non-verbal thought processes. These include pattern recognition, perception of depth, colour and other visual relations, the appreciation of rhythm and music, and creative expression.

Are these areas in which you feel comfortable? Theorists point out that a traditional education tends to foster left-brain activities such as reading, writing and arithmetic and often undervalues and undermines students who naturally excel in right-brain activities. Perhaps you lack confidence in 'right-brain' activities because you have never been encouraged to develop your skills? Or perhaps you are self-doubting in typical 'left-brain' activities because your school did not value your typically right-brain skills and allowed you to think you were just 'no good' at school work.

Either way, the news is good. You can raise the performance of your weaker brain hemisphere. When the less active of the two hemispheres is stimulated, its performance greatly improves, and the brain's overall effectiveness shoots up.

The 'creative' right brain In general, the left brain/right brain distinction is often used very imprecisely. The right brain is seen as the seat of instinctive, intuitive thought and creative impulses, while the left brain brings – sometimes stifling – critical analysis to bear. Writers suggest that we need to develop and unleash the power of the right brain. There is a kernel of truth within this kind of analysis, but it is overblown and misrepresents the carefully drawn distinction between left and right hemisphere specializations.

Mind maps Building on the left brain/right brain theory, mind expert Tony Buzan developed 'mind maps' as a form of note-taking that engaged both halves of the brain, thereby improving listening skills and so greatly increasing a person's capacity to learn and to retrieve information. The process combines keywords from the subject being discussed with various visual cues to create a memorable 'map' of relevant facts. Buzan suggests using arrows, different writing sizes and styles, colours and drawings to create a mind map.

The whole brain

Some experts caution that the right-brain/left-brain division is an oversimplification. Modern research indicates that complex mental activities are never entirely isolated in one part of the brain. Instead they involve many parts of the brain working together simultaneously.

The left and right cerebral hemispheres never function in isolation. They are connected by a bundle of three hundred million nerve fibres named the corpus callosum. The two sides complement and support one other. In the course of the brain's evolution the corpus callosum has grown steadily thicker, suggesting – according to some experts – that we have developed ever greater integration between the two halves of the brain and their roles in mental functions.

Using both right and left brains Many of the greatest figures in scientific and cultural history are notable for their capacity to use mental abilities associated with both sides of the brain. Albert Einstein reputedly grasped the truth behind his ground-breaking Theory of Relativity not in some dusty experimental laboratory, but in a moment of daydreaming idleness on a sunny hillside when he was imagining what it would be like to travel along a sunbeam. He then used left-brain dominant scientific method to work out and communicate his right-brain insight.

Equally, the artist Pablo Picasso expressed in his notebooks a precise geometrical understanding of what he was doing on canvas. Even more extraordinary was the great Italian Renaissance man Leonardo da Vinci, creator of the *Mona Lisa*, who had ability as a mathematician and logician that matched or even exceeded his excellence as an artist.

Use the exercises that follow to develop your awareness of your own ability in typically left-brain and right-brain activities such as logic or spatial perception. Practise and keep on practising to boost your confidence in areas you find a major challenge. Develop your capacity to use both sides of your brain and unleash a little of the enormous creativity and power enjoyed by an Einstein, a Picasso or a Leonardo.

Exercise 1 LEFT/RIGHT-BRAIN EXERCISE

Consider the following. Which apply to you? Note any that ring true, then check the answers at the back. If you get more Rs you are considered a right-brain thinker; more Ls, and your left brain is your stronger side.

1 I constantly look at a clock or wear a watch
2 I keep a journal or diary of my thoughts
3 I believe there is a right or a wrong way to do everything
4 I find it hard to follow directions precisely
5 'Life is just a bowl of cherries' makes no sense to me
6 I frequently change my plans and find that sticking to a schedule is boring
7 It's easier to draw a map than explain how to get somewhere
8 To find a lost item, I try to picture it in my head where I last saw it
9 I frequently let my emotions guide me
10 I learn maths with ease
11 I'd read the directions before assembling something
12 People tell me I am always late getting places
13 People have told me that I'm psychic
14 I need to set goals for myself to keep me on track
15 When somebody asks me a question, I turn my head to the left

16 If I have a tough decision to make, I write down the pros and the cons

17 I'd probably make a good detective

18 I learn music with ease

19 To solve a problem, I think of similar problems I have solved in the past

20 I use a lot of gestures

21 If someone asks me a question, I turn my head to the right

22 I believe there are two ways to look at almost everything

23 I have the ability to tell if people are lying or guilty of something, just by looking at them

24 I keep a 'to-do' list

25 I am able to explain thoroughly my opinions in words

26 In a debate, I am objective and look at the facts before forming an opinion

27 I've considered becoming a poet, a politician, an architect or a dancer

28 I always lose track of time

29 When trying to remember a name I forgot, I'd recite the alphabet until I remembered it

30 I like to draw

31 When I'm confused, I usually go with my gut instinct

32 I have considered becoming a lawyer, journalist, or doctor

Exercise 2 IT'S NEVER BLACK OR WHITE
Can you override your ability to read? First, read out the words then say whether each is white, black or grey. It's harder to shut off the word-based part of our brain as it's the most easily assimilated piece of information.

BLACK	GREY	WHITE
GREY	WHITE	BLACK
WHITE	**BLACK**	**WHITE**
BLACK	BLACK	GREY
GREY	GREY	**WHITE**
BLACK	**WHITE**	BLACK

Exercise 3 ONLY ODDITY?
Think quickly: which is the 'obvious' odd one out?

Exercise 4 ROUTE MASTER
Different people will tackle this route-planning test in different ways. There is no one correct answer.

What is the SIMPLEST set of instructions you could give someone to explain how to travel from A to B? The length of the journey doesn't matter, simplicity is the key.

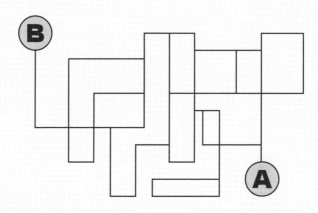

Music and memory

Brainwaves are a record of electrical activity in the brain as measured by an electroencephalograph (EEG) machine. Researchers have identified which brainwave levels accompany peak-performance mental states.

As we have seen (*pages 16–17*), when you are in the state of full alertness necessary for working out a complex problem you have beta brainwaves (between 14 and 40 cycles per second). When you are in the state of relaxed receptiveness perfect for studying and learning you have alpha brainwaves (9 to 14 cycles per second).

Certain kinds of music appear to lead the brain to a level of activity that accompanies relaxed alertness. Music from the Baroque and Classical eras (from the 17th century to the early 19th century) by composers such as Mozart, J. S. Bach, Pachelbel, Vivaldi, Albinoni and Haydn has been proven to help students learn and recall complex material.

A piece of slow music from the Baroque era tends to have around 60 beats per minute. In a trial it was shown to slow the heart beat and reduce blood pressure, to lower beta brainwaves and increase relaxed alpha brainwaves. Studying while listening to this music engaged both sides of the upper brain, and so improved the performance of the whole brain.

Benefit of exercise Outdoor running often produces theta brainwaves (5 to 8 cycles per second), which are conducive to creative thinking – people in theta often have good ideas, and allow them to flow. Aerobic exercise also increases brain levels of BDNF (brain-derived neurotrophic factor), a chemical that boosts the growth of neurons and brain cell connections (*see page 71*), and of serotonin, another chemical that helps neuron growth and lifts your mood.

The exercises that follow allow you to experiment with the effects of music on your powers of attention and recall.

PRODUCTIVE LAYERS
Research has shown that hens lay more eggs when played classical music, such as 'The Blue Danube Waltz' by Johann Strauss.

Exercise 5 MOZART, MILES DAVIS AND THE RAMONES
The purpose of this exercise is to discover how music affects your brainpower.

Choose three pieces of music – one classical (preferably 18th-century, such as Mozart or J. S. Bach), one jazz and one rock. Take three quite challenging pieces of reading: read one with each type of music, then try to list as many facts as you can an hour afterwards. Was your performance better with a particular type of music? Researchers have discovered that listening to 18th-century classical music – such as Bach or Mozart – improves short- and long-term memory. The music fosters a state of relaxed alertness, reducing beta brainwaves (14 to 40 cycles a second) and promoting relaxed alpha waves (9 to 14 cycles a second). This is perfect for studying.

Exercise 6 BAROQUE FACT TEST
Find a slow piece of Baroque-era music (the Largo movement from the 'Winter' section of *The Four Seasons* by Vivaldi, or the Canon in D by Pachelbel perhaps).

Choose two short encyclopedia entries on subjects you know little about. Read and try to learn the first while listening to the music, then read and learn the second without music. Test your powers of recall, and compare your performance. Brain scientists report that studying while listening to music engages both right and left hemispheres of the upper brain, and so improves the performance of the whole brain.

Exercise 7 CLASSICAL MEMORY BOOST
Repeat Exercise 6 with two newspaper articles.

This time when you test your powers of recall, do so in silence for one article but while listening to your chosen Baroque music for the second. How did your performance compare? Memory experts suggest that when attempting to recall something you have learnt it helps to recreate the conditions in which you learnt it – for example, by listening to the same music.

Exercise 8 MUSICAL POWER NAP
Set yourself a personal challenge – for some, this might be a cryptic crossword, for others a maths problem.

Work on your challenge for ten minutes. Then take a break: sit quietly, listening to a piece of classical music by Mozart, J. S. Bach, Josef Haydn or similar. Let your thoughts wander. Return to the puzzle and see how your performance compares. When doing something you find really difficult, your work is often inhibited by anxiety. A musical power nap may improve mental performance by boosting the alpha brainwaves that accompany alert relaxation.

Visual–spatial skills

Visual–spatial skills are survival skills. Every moment you are awake, your brain – in combination with your sense organs and inputs from the nervous system – is negotiating your body's relationship with its immediate environment.

You need a full array of visual–spatial skills just to get through the first few minutes of each day. Without them, you wouldn't be able to judge the distance from your bed to the floor, you would bump into the furniture as you tried to leave the room, you would be unable to pour coffee into a mug or lift the mug to your lips.

You wouldn't recognize your nearest and dearest – because you need visual recognition skills to make sense of the combination of nose, ears, chin and eyes as a familiar face. To cap it all, even if you managed to make it out of the house, you'd be likely to drive your car into the garage wall or be knocked down by a bus as you crossed the road.

Beyond this, visual–spatial skills enable you to perform an enormous range of activities at work and leisure. With these skills, you decipher a map or locate yourself in unfamiliar physical surroundings, such as a conference hall or a railway station. They enable you to write neatly, to place numbers in columns to do a calculation, to lay out information in a presentation or for a mailshot. With these abilities you can understand systems such as flowcharts and computer networks, or work out the relationship of the parts to a whole – for example, when trying to mend your bicycle or fix a lock on the door of your office.

Improving visual–spatial skills boosts thinking power An eye for detail raises your powers of perception. When you are studying or memorizing information, visualization helps you to input information in a memorable form and to recall it later. As you develop the ability to see things in groups, and to understand the relation of the parts to the whole, you are engaging the right hemisphere of the upper brain and beginning to develop the whole-brain performance that is the key to the highest achievement.

Thinking in three dimensions

If you are moving a table around a difficult corner on a staircase, do you find it easy to see if it will fit? If you have to arrange several pieces of furniture in a small room can you quickly visualize the best arrangement? Can you take apart and put back together the parts of a complex assembly – such as a car engine? If the answer to these questions is an enthusiastic 'Yes', then you are naturally blessed with strong visual–spatial skills; if 'No', then – like me – you need practice to develop this area of your intelligence.

Learning through playing Doing puzzles and games is both a fun and an efficient way to 'grow' your visual–spatial skills. Playing with children's building blocks develops your ability to visualize the relations of objects in three dimensions.

Maze puzzles practise your visual tracking skills. By doing spot the difference games or complete the set tests you develop a discriminating eye for detail. Jigsaws enhance your visual powers and your ability to fit parts into a whole.

Create your own exercises Along with verbal-linguistic ability, numerical know-how, and logical and analytical expertise, visual–spatial skills are a key aspect of intelligence – and one that you can certainly improve with practice. Try creating your own exercises. Take a simple cube, such as one of the dice from a board game. Draw a two-dimensional plan of the cube, flat on the paper so that all its six surfaces are visible. Then, in your mind's eye, imagine creating the cube from the two-dimensional plan. Such techniques boost your capacity for visualization and your ability to 'think' in three dimensions.

Use the exercises on the pages that follow to hone your eye for detail and your ability to see spatial relations. Power up your capacity for visual imagination.

SLOWLY DOES IT
Be patient. Don't rush at puzzles but approach them slowly, with a keen eye and your logical thinking cap on. If you don't succeed first time, come back and try again later.

Exercise 9 BEEF IT UP

When trying to imagine something, perhaps when using memory systems, there is much you can do to strengthen the image. Try the visual techniques below.

A weak image runs the risk of losing the vital connection and hence you forget the information. As well as the traditional five senses, think about: humour, optimism (positive images are remembered better), sex (no one will know!), exaggeration, your viewpoint in the image, movement, symbolism and wordplay – useful for abstract concepts that can't be imagined easily.

Exercise 10 GOAL-GETTER

All of us have major goals that we want to achieve. Using visualization techniques can help you get there.

Can you visualize yourself in the position you want to be in? What time of year is it? What are you wearing and who are you with? Are you at a special event? Now work backwards from that goal. What intermediate steps do you need to take? Can you visualize yourself halfway to your goal? All motivation experts agree – without visualizing your goal, writing it down and planning for it, it's nearly impossible to achieve it. Practising this type of technique also helps keep your mind sharp.

Exercise 11 BUSINESS SENSE

All too often, businesses and projects fail due to simple common sense. Visual acuity is beneficial. Try this.

Most people are involved in some kind of commercial activity. Imagine yourself as the customer and clear your thoughts entirely. Suppose you run a clothing store. Is it clear from the name or outside of the shop that you sell women's clothes? Can the customer see that you have a sale on at the moment? Why are the size labels so difficult to see? Why is your website address so difficult to remember? Visualize the problems first and solve them for your customer. Then practise this technique for other aspects of your life.

Exercise 12 CARTOON FUN

Cartoon characters frequently make use of unusual methods to solve problems, and therein lies much of the comedy.

Suppose you had to retrieve an object frozen inside a large block of ice. Ordinary people might use a chisel or saw. Free yourself from the usual trains of thought by imagining yourself as a reckless cartoon character or a robot. Could you use the oven? A drill? Why not throw the ice off the roof? Look for valid solutions outside the everyday 'I would usually …' sphere. This will also help you train the lateral side of your brain.

Puzzle 39 NUMBER BREAKDOWN

Look at this square. Using your eyes only, can you divide it into four identical smaller sections, each composed of sixteen smaller squares and containing four different numbers?

	1				2		3
				3		1	
		2	4	4			
	1						
		2				2	
				4			
3			3			1	
		4					

Puzzle 40 SCENIC SURPRISE

Eyes ready! There are seven differences between these two pictures. Can you spot them? Circle them in the lower drawing.

Puzzle 41 SEW EASY?

Can you see which needle is threaded through which button? Try doing the maze first time round using only your eyes rather than your finger or a pencil. Can you reach the correct conclusion without losing the thread?

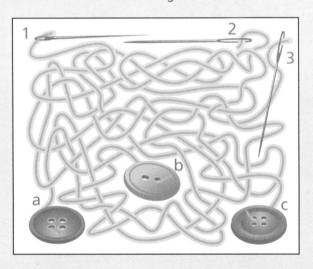

Puzzle 42 CHICKEN AND EGG

Utilize your powers of visual reasoning to work out which of the boxed images on the right completes the set on the left.

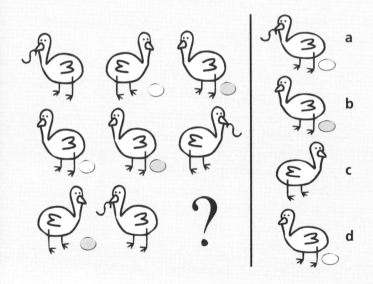

Using language

Think back over your activities of today (or yesterday). List ten ways in which you relied on words as you went about your business. You probably read the labelling on the coffee packet, breakfast cereal or jam jar. Perhaps you spoke to your children. Did you read the newspaper, listen to the radio or TV news, speak to the man in the coffee shop, discuss work matters with a colleague, text a friend, email your mother? Perhaps you had to read and fill out a form?

Now imagine you wake up tomorrow and have lost your ability to understand and use language, or have been transported to a land whose people speak only their own incomprehensible tongue. You will have a graphic – and unpleasant – demonstration of how essential linguistic skills are.

Of course we also need language for thinking – for organizing and recalling information. Improving linguistic ability greatly increases our thinking power and mental performance.

An essential aspect of mental work is being self-aware – monitoring what you are doing. Language appears to play a key role in this activity. The brain's left frontal lobe takes a dominant part in managing the brain's activities, and if necessary redirecting attention or choosing a new strategy. The left frontal lobe is closely associated with the language and speech areas of the upper brain's left hemisphere.

A running commentary Drivers of emergency vehicles are trained to make a running description of what they are doing. The driver speaks aloud, saying things like 'heading south on A82, am approaching turn-off, will slow down', and so on. This verbalizing keeps them hyper-alert. I sometimes do something similar when pulling off a complicated activity such as cooking a family dinner at speed – 'I will put the water on for the pasta, then chop the garlic and onions. But first I should check whether we have enough tomatoes' etc.

The ability to choose the right words and use them accurately is essential for clear thinking. And taking pleasure in the rules and engagements of language gives you plenty of tools for receiving, handling and dispensing facts and opinions.

Developing word skills

Do you like reading? Do you enjoy foreign languages? Do you take pleasure in solving crossword puzzles, proving your spelling prowess or working out anagrams? When you're memorizing information, do you find it easier to recall words or use a mnemonic such as All Cows Eat Grass (*see page 73*) rather than to visualize the facts associated with the words?

Some people have a natural affinity for words and for linguistic self-expression. Because they enjoy reading and immerse themselves in language, they understand the rules of grammar and spelling. They have an ability to 'see' the correct spellings for words and have a 'feel' for the best arrangement of words. Others find spelling, grammar and syntax much more of a challenge. But we can all develop our linguistic skills by practising them – and so creating new networks in and among language areas of the brain.

Having fun with words Playing with language using spelling games, crosswords, word-category games, anagrams, riddles and so on boosts your vocabulary, enhances your ability to recognize and deploy the right words, and builds your capacity for organizing words and parts of words.

Practice of this kind greatly enhances your powers of recall. Organizing information into lists or bullet points and playing verbal games with facts by creating mnemonics or A–Z lists, say, are key memory tricks.

Language games also improve your ability to spot patterns. For this reason, they are a good example of cross-training the brain, for they boost your number-handling skills as well as your ability to understand and visualize complex processes. Forging connections between diverse brain areas, language puzzles train your intelligence and safeguard your thinking in future by helping to maintain an active and cross-connected brain.

Use the exercises and puzzles on the pages that follow to create and renew connections among the neurons in your brain's vital language areas. And, most importantly, learn from any mistakes!

Exercise 13 NIGHT FRIGHT ON THE DOORSTEP
How's your spelling? See if you can identify and correct all 13 'howlers' in this shivery short story to test whether your spellings passes muster. Why not make up spelling tests of your own to try on other people. You will learn a lot yourself from the exercise.

Hearing a horendous moaning, Jim wrenched open the front door. He recieved a terrible fright when he saw three miniscule ghosts dancing before him.

'We come from the cemetary,' a voice said. 'We are the wierd battallion,' a second added. 'We are spirits desparate for sustenence,' said another. Something clicked in Jim's mind, as he remembered the date. 'This is quite a developement,' he said cooly.

'Trick or Treat!' the three boys yelled. 'Can I reccomend one of these?' Jim replied. 'They are irresistable.' He held out a bowel of sweets.

Exercise 14 ONE IN THREE
Choose the correctly spelled word in each of these triple challenges. It's usually best to go with your first instinct. No dictionaries allowed!

1	acommodate	accomodate	accommodate
2	milenium	millennium	millenium
3	harras	harass	harrass
4	consensus	concensus	conscensus
5	exceed	excede	exscede
6	innocculate	inoculate	innoculate
7	momento	mumento	memento
8	repetition	repitition	repitetion

Exercise 15 ALPHABET FRUIT BOWL
Play this game with a couple of friends or family members – or take all the parts yourself, if you prefer.

The aim is to create an exotic fruit bowl, containing fruits beginning with as many letters of the alphabet as possible. Player 1 nominates a fruit beginning with A, Player 2 names one beginning with B, Player 3 suggests one beginning with C, and so on. Score 3 points for a fruit beginning with the correct letter, 2 for one where the correct letter is the second letter in the name and 1 point for a fruit containing the correct letter. This game will stretch your vocabulary and spelling intelligence.

Exercise 16 WHEELBARROW WORDS
Test your skills at unravelling letters. Perhaps you're a real whiz at anagrams? If so, why not try making up some of your own to test out friends and family.

Frank the gardener had trouble spelling, so he got into the habit of cutting out the letters of gardening words he wanted to learn to spell and stuck them to his wheelbarrow – one word on each handle, one on each of the wheels, and one along the end rim. Up rose the wind and blew the letters off. Can you help Frank sort them out in this test of your anagramming skills?

First handle:	r – a – g – e – r – n – e – d
Second handle:	r – l – n – w – e – m – o – w – a
One wheel:	e – h – s – p – e – o – i – p
Other wheel:	r – p – i – l – n – s – r – e – k
End rim:	e – a – p – d – s

Exercise 17 WORD TENNIS

Word tennis tests the vocabulary and general word-handling, and can be played in two- or one-player versions.

For Two: The two players bat words back and forward like tennis players hitting a ball over the net. You might start by batting words beginning with the same two letters. You say 'Love', your opponent can reply with any word starting with 'Lo' ('Locust', 'Loop'). Then change to batting opposites: you say 'tall', your opponent says 'short'.

It helps to have an umpire, who can call out the switches in category. Have a strict time limit for replying, such as ten seconds. If player 2 cannot think of a response, player 1 wins the point and vice versa. For your first game, bat words in these categories: **1** Words sharing first two letters. **2** Opposites. **3** People's names ending with same letter. **4** City names beginning with same first letter. **5** Synonyms. You can also make up your own categories.

For One: In the solitaire version, you have to think of four words in each category within a set time, say ten seconds.

Puzzle 43 MISSING PRESIDENT

Place the names of these US presidents in the horizontal rows of the grid so that the shaded squares, in order from the top, spell out the name of another president.

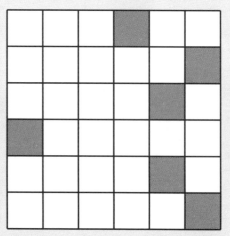

REAGAN   CARTER   HOOVER
ARTHUR   MONROE   WILSON

Puzzle 44 LANGUAGE BARRIER III

See how quickly you can use your linguistic skills and your powers of reasoning to uncover the missing artists below.

If Picasso is CEMYHHI,

Rembrandt is ZATQZYVJK

and Van Gogh is BYV PIPW …

then who are

TIVAK, TYKEHHA

and JAPYH?

Learning to love numbers

Many people allow their brains to close down when they're asked to perform quite basic maths problems. They view number-crunching puzzles with incomprehension, almost as the products of a foreign language.

In fact there are similarities between the capacity to juggle numbers and a facility with words. Both require mental dexterity and skills in seeing patterns in the world around us.

Perhaps people who dislike numbers were 'turned off' maths by overly strict teachers or maybe they've just allowed their mental maths machinery to grow rusty, so they find they simply can't do quick calculations. If you are one of these folk, why not make a new start? Stop worrying and learn to love numbers. The 'language' of maths has an undeniable

---

HOW MANY SECONDS IN A MILLION?
If you were to start counting at a rate of a hundred numbers a minute, and continue without stopping, it would take almost a week (more than 6 days 22 hours) to count to a million.

beauty and elegance. And as with the other areas of brain-power, practice makes all the difference – you'll be amazed how much you improve if you train your maths brain.

Patterns and proportions We are born brimful of curiosity. Biologists suggest that curiosity about our environment is closely allied to our survival instinct – we are hard-wired to investigate the world around us. From observation of children I would say that most – if not all – of us come into the world with love of numbers, a taste for counting things and making patterns.

Mathematical patterns abound in nature. For example, the spirals of seeds in the head of a sunflower follow the Fibonacci sequence of numbers – a sequence (beginning 1, 1, 2, 3, 5, 8, 13, 21, 34, 55, 89) in which after the first two figures each is the sum of the two previous ones; if one spiral has 55 seeds, the next will have 89 and so on. It is named after the medieval Italian mathematician Leonardo Fibonacci, who used it to solve a puzzle about rabbits breeding.

Everyday maths

A street vendor sells you a snack – a drink and a piece of fruit – and names the price. Are you the kind of person who can quickly tot up the prices of the items to check that his addition is correct?

A capacity to do mental maths can be a key part of thinking on your feet. Perhaps you're having a discussion with your boss about interest rates or another economic indicator, and have to do a silent calculation before making a point – you need to be able to juggle figures to pull the trick off. Equally you may have to check a currency conver-

---

THE ANSWER IS 1089, WHAT'S THE QUESTION?
Take ANY three-digit number in which the first digit is larger than the third, say, 834. This is A. Write it backwards (438). This is B. Subtract B (438) from A (834). That gives you 396. This is C. (If C is two digits rather than three, e.g. 99, add a 0 in front, so 099.) Reverse 396. That gives you 693. This is D. Add D (693) and C (396). The answer, as I said, is 1089. This works with every three-digit number in which the first is larger than the last.

---

sion while on holiday, or work out the correct proportions of ingredients when you're not following a recipe exactly as written. Whatever we may think, there's no avoiding maths.

Use the puzzles on the pages that follow as a workout for the number-crunching areas of your brain. Put in some time doing Sudoku squares and number puzzles from books and newspapers. In everyday situations, practise doing calculations in your head rather than with the aid of a calculator. Try playing quick-fire calculation games with your children, your partner or your housemates over the breakfast or dinner table.

Even if maths doesn't come naturally, don't let your number powers lie dormant. Keeping your brain active in the maths zone will enhance your performance in all other areas of brain work – in your job or at school, doing cross-words, reading and memorizing, discussing weighty political or religious matters, even in thinking laterally and creatively. Make sure your maths muscles are toned. Earn your passport to the brave new world of the mathemagicians.

Exercise 18 FIZZ BUZZ

A great way to gain confidence with numbers is to play a game of Fizz Buzz. Beware: it can become compelling.

Players take turns to count the numbers 1, 2, 3, 4, 5 etc. However, multiples of 3 must be replaced by Fizz and multiples of 4 by Buzz. A game would therefore start: '1, 2, Fizz, Buzz, 5, Fizz, 7, Buzz, Fizz, 10, 11, Fizz Buzz, 13 …' and so on. How far can you go before you make a mistake? Play the game with different multiples, or even introduce a third word for, say, multiples of 7.

Exercise 19 LETTERS AND NUMBERS

This is a challenging mental exercise to try and combines a bit of letter know-how with arithmetic skills.

ONE has three letters, so add 3 to get 4. FOUR has four letters. 4+4 = 8. EIGHT + 5 (five letters) gives …? How quickly can you continue this sequence? If you're very good, you could reach up to 95 or beyond. Time yourself then see how fast your friends do it. Now consider making up your own games, perhaps taking turns with another player – for example, add '1' for every vowel or straight line in the spelt-out number.

Exercise 20 THE 3–9 TRICK

One of the best ways to start enjoying numbers is to explore the beauty of their symmetry. Start here.

To see if a number is divisible by 3, add up the digits. Keep adding until you get down to one digit. If that number is 3, 6 or 9, the number is divisible by 3 (for example, 11,847 totals 21 which totals 3, so 11,847 is a multiple of 3). The same works for numbers divisible by 9 – if the digit sum is 9, the number is divisible by 9. Now test yourself by writing down random numbers (or getting a friend to do it). How quickly you can determine if it's divisible by 3 and/or 9?

Exercise 21 X MARKS THE SPOT

This is another exercise that illustrates how numbers can often surprise us.

To add up the numbers from 1 to X, add one to X, multiply this by X itself, then divide by 2. For example, 1, 2, 3, 4, 5 and 6 add up to (7x6)/2 = 42/2 = 21. To see why this works, note how we can rearrange the list as three pairs of 7: (1+6), (2+5) and (3+4). This shortcut was noticed by the mathematician Gauss when he was a schoolboy. Can you now total the numbers on a telephone (0 to 9) or a dartboard (1 to 20)?

Puzzle 45 NUMBER DIVIDER

Do these numbers have something in common? If you think hard, you'll discover that they can all be divided equally by one number, which you should write in the middle box. See if you can work it out in your head, without resorting to the aid of a calculator.

171		114
266	?	475
817		1311

Puzzle 46 WEIGH IT UP

Each of the symbols below has a certain weight. You can see that scales a and b balance perfectly, and from that you should be able to work out how many circles you would need to balance scale c.

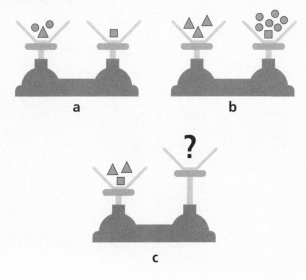

Puzzle 47 HIDDEN NUMBER

The number **5,532,917** can be found once and once only in the grid. It may be read up, down, forward or backwards, or even diagonally. Can you track it down?

5	3	5	5	3	5	9	7	1	9	2	5
9	5	5	3	3	5	7	9	2	8	5	3
2	7	3	5	7	3	1	9	2	3	5	5
7	8	2	3	3	2	9	2	9	2	3	2
3	7	9	7	9	9	7	1	2	3	2	5
2	2	1	1	2	1	7	9	9	3	9	7
3	2	8	9	3	9	2	7	2	2	5	9
5	3	4	2	2	7	2	9	1	7	1	5
5	7	6	3	3	9	3	3	2	7	9	2
9	3	5	5	3	7	9	9	5	3	3	3
2	5	5	5	9	2	2	7	4	5	5	5
5	5	3	2	9	7	1	1	2	3	5	5

Puzzle 48 FUN WITH NUMBERS

Every row and column of this number grid contains the same numbers and mathematical symbols, but in a different order each time. Engage your mathematical brain to work out how to arrive at the correct totals shown below.

19	−	10	x	20	+	32	=	212
							=	178
							=	139
							=	330
=		=		=		=		
908		202		501		310		

167

The basis of memory training

Ancient peoples were memory experts. In a period when most people were illiterate, long before the invention of printing, tribal history had to be memorized and passed orally from generation to generation. Epic poems and religious scriptures were also transmitted by mouth.

As a result, feats of memory in that world were prodigious. The ancient Greek epic *The Iliad*, for example, has sixteen thousand verses and must have taken four or five evenings to recite. The ancient Indian epic, the *Mahabharata*, is even longer – a hundred thousand verses in its entirety. These narratives were doubtless embroidered in the telling, and no two performances would have been the same.

But ancient Indian priests believed that their extensive and very ancient scriptures – Vedas – had to be learned, remembered and recited 100 per cent word perfect. Otherwise, the gods might be angered and the balance of the cosmos disturbed. The priests developed a complex rote-learning pattern. The words 'we meditate on the blessed shining of the sun god' would have been learnt as follows: 'we meditate, meditate we, we meditate on, on meditate we, we meditate on, meditate on, on meditate, meditate on the' and so on. The result, experts believe, is an ancient oral scripture whose words remain remarkably close to the original.

Processing power Modern memory experts have learned from ancient Indian devotees. They tell us that the more we activate the brain to process information we want to recall, the easier we will find it to remember.

Imagine you want to learn these words: cat, table, coat, cushion, cow, bread, lettuce, scarf, coffee, rose, suit. Categorizing the elements will help you remember them. For example, divide them as follows: living things (cat, cow, rose); foods or drinks (bread, lettuce, coffee); clothes (coat, scarf, suit); furniture (table, cushion).

The more areas of our brains we activate, the better we remember. Try linking words in the list to a smell (rose, bread, coffee) or to a touch (bread, scarf, cushion – soft; table – hard).

Release your brain power

It is a fact of life that people are born with differing levels of ability. Some have a gift for tennis, others music, others writing, and so on. But, given good health and normal development, we all have brains of prodigious capacity and force at our disposal. We can all learn how to use a little more of the largely untapped power contained in our thinking organs. A key way to begin doing this is by training the memory.

We've probably all struggled to learn lists of dry facts such as chemical symbols or historical dates. The trick is to bring the dry facts alive. If the information makes a vivid impression, it will be much easier to remember. Try associating facts with film stars, sportspeople or relatives – or with anything that appeals to you: flower types, rock bands, cities ...

Say you are a visiting student and have to learn this sequence of westerly US states: Washington, Oregon, California, Idaho, Nevada, Utah, Arizona. How about seven movies: *Wolf Man*, *On the Waterfront*, *Citizen Kane*, *Intolerance*, *North by Northwest*, *Unforgiven*, *Alien*?

The power of association If you're struggling to recall a fact, try instead to remember some aspect associated with learning the information, such as where you were, how you felt or who you were with. As we have seen (*pages 136–7*), evidence suggests that if you learn something while listening to a CD of classical music, playing the CD again will help you bring to mind what you learnt. The same power of association kicks in if you recall a smell, a place, even an emotional state that you associate with the information.

Memory walk If you have to learn a list of facts or sequence of images, associate each one with a place on a walk you know well. In your mind's eye, follow the walk and you will encounter each of the facts. Generally it helps to connect what you are learning to what you already know.

MEMORY TRIGGER
If you can't remember your boss's husband's name, try to recall where you met him, how he was standing, how you felt that day.

Memory training for everyday life

Do your powers of recall let you down? With brain training you can turn your memory into a powerful ally. Imagine you're at work and encounter several new colleagues in a meeting, and they go quickly round the table introducing themselves. Or you walk into a room at a party and are introduced swiftly to four strangers in turn. Do you experience a blur of faces and a whirl of names, or can you remember these new names sufficiently well to make relaxed small talk or hold a business discussion?

Memory training techniques can help you attach names to faces and fix people's identity in your short-term memory – greatly improving your self-presentation as an alert, capable and engaging individual! First of all, be attentive. Be sure to listen carefully when being introduced and don't panic.

BE POSITIVE!
Don't be defeatist. If you believe that your powers of recall are poor or failing, then you will inhibit your memory performance.

Second, try to make a conscious link in your mind between the person's name and his or her features. If you can think of some visually powerful or humorous link between the two, so much the better. If your colleague is named, say, Alan Ball, try visualizing him for a moment as a giant beach ball.

Look briefly at each face in turn and repeat the name. This will reinforce your 'learning' of your new friends' identity. If necessary, check the correct pronunciation of the name with the person. Then when you are talking, use people's names as another way of reinforcing your learning.

Everyday forgetfulness Lost your keys? Forgotten the bay in which you parked your car? One simple brainpower strategy is to verbalize what you are doing as you do it. Often you 'forget' something because you were not fully attentive when you performed it. Say aloud, or under your breath: 'I am putting the car keys in my left-hand pocket' or 'I am parking in Car Park 5, Level A'.

Making memory training work for you

There are many types of memory training for you to try. Choose according to your thinking style and existing mental strengths – you may prefer visualization, imagining facts as stages on a walk, categorizing information by word or letter groups, or dividing it on a numerical basis. Experiment, and find which strategies work best for you.

If you have several things to learn, go for variety. If you are studying and have to revise your Spanish vocabulary, your biology coursework and your history dates, it is better to spend one hour on Spanish, then one on biology and one on history for three consecutive days rather than do the three subjects in long, three-hour blocks on separate days.

Don't overdo it. As we have seen, being relaxed greatly helps you learn and recall information. If you are very tired, take a break.

For a few moments do something different and unexpected. If you are working at home and stop for a coffee, do some stretches or have a quick dance in the kitchen while the water's boiling. In an office block take another route to the coffee machine or walk to a new shop or cafe to order your cappuccino.

The puzzling way Doing puzzles is a key way to practise paying full attention. You strengthen your powers of recall and raise performance levels throughout the brain by testing and stretching it with mental and visual-manipulative games, including the wooden puzzle included in the *Brain Box*.

Use the puzzles on the pages that follow to practise your favoured methods of memory training – and test their effectiveness. Keep exercising your memorizing and recall skills. Watch for improvements in your everyday memory over the next few weeks. Are you finding it easier to memorize your shopping list? Have you stopped losing your keys?

PAY ATTENTION!
Remind yourself how important it is to be attentive when listening or learning information.

Exercise 22 EXAGGERATION

A vital part of memory skills is to tap into your imagination. Try this exercise to get it going.

Use things big and dramatic. 'See' the vivid colours, and imagine loud noises. For example, if you need to remember to feed the neighbour's cat in the morning, put a toy or your slippers by the bedroom door. Imagine that turning into a loud, roaring hungry lion with a golden mane. In the morning, your brain should replay that association in your mind's eye and you won't forget!

Exercise 23 MNEMONICS

Everyone knows '30 days have September ...' Mnemonics – rhymes or phrases used as memory joggers – can be used for many things.

The planets of the Solar System can be remembered by: My Very Easy Method Just Speeds Up Naming Planets (Mercury, Venus, Earth, Mars, Jupiter, Saturn, Uranus, Neptune, Pluto). If there's something you often confuse or forget, make up a mnemonic of your own. It doesn't have to be an 'official' mnemonic, and it can be as cheeky as you like! The main thing is that it works for you.

Exercise 24 THE ROMAN ROOM SYSTEM

This is a tried-and-tested memory technique used by the ancient Romans.

Suppose you need to buy pasta, wrapping paper, ink and a camera on a shopping trip. Imagine a trip around your house: you see tubes of pasta instead of balustrades on your staircase, everything in your lounge wrapped in paper, ink flooding out of your sink and a paparazzo holding a photo shoot in your bedroom. If you forget an item during your shopping trip, replay this journey in your mind.

Exercise 25 THE CHAIN SYSTEM

This story system will help you remember lists and can easily be extended to 100 items or more. Have a go!

How to remember a list such as: Father, Spoon, Green, Basketball, Friday? Imagine one item interacting with the next in the most bizarre way possible. Start with your father inside a giant spoon, then visualize the spoon gouging a crater out of a golfing green. A ball comes out of the hole but it's not a golf ball, it's a basketball. It rises out of the air and lands on the head of Robinson Crusoe's Man Friday.

Exercise 26 SHAPE-HOOK SYSTEM

Here's another system for remembering lists, but this allows you to remember an item without going through the entire list. Too good to be true? Try it and find out.

Objects can resemble numbers: 1 = sword, 2 = swan, 3 = heart, 4 = yacht, 5 = meat hook, 6 = golf club, 7 = cliff, 8 = egg-timer, 9 = balloon, 10 = knife and plate. To remember ten items and recall them in any order, link each item with the appropriate object. For example, if the fifth thing you need to do today is service the car, imagine your car hanging up in the air on a meat hook. Practise this efficient system and you'll be abe to remember a particular item without having to recall every single one.

Exercise 27 SHAPE-RHYME SYSTEM

A rhyming scheme may also help you remember lists.

Start with, for example, 1 = gun, 2 = shoe, 3 = tree, 4 = door, 5 = (bee)hive, 6 = sticks, 7 = heaven, 8 = gate, 9 = lime, 10 = hen. This makes it very easy to recall the objects which you need to link to your own list of items. Suppose you are giving a speech and your sixth item is about job cuts. Sixth rhymes with sticks. Now link sticks with job cuts in your imagination – maybe sharp sticks are scratching Job from the Bible, or think of a tree surgeon whose job is to cut sticks.

Exercise 28 FOREIGN LANGUAGES

Many people find learning a foreign language formidable. The trick is to link words together, like this.

'Maintenant' is French for 'now'. So, imagine you are a landlord and you go to the house to ask the main tenant for your rent money now. See the house in your mind's eye, and how angry you are that you don't already have the money! You want it NOW! Try this exercise for 'flasche' (German for bottle) and 'catarata' (Spanish for waterfall).

Exercise 29 NAMES TO FACES

One of the most common memory problems is to do with remembering people's names. Use this technique if your memory sometimes needs jogging.

To remember people's names, find a word link with their name (forename or surname) then imagining 'warping' their face to fit that image. Look for the most distinctive feature about someone. If a lady with big hair is called Mrs Walker, imagine her hair turning into a dog that she's taking for a walk. It's vital that you hear their name correctly. Don't be embarrassed to ask someone to repeat their name two or three times – better to get it right third time than to forget in the future.

Exercise 30 SPIDER DIAGRAMS

To brainstorm for ideas, research a topic or remember a speech, you can start with your central idea in the middle of a piece of paper then 'branch out' into the different areas.

This tree structure is more interesting than a list, and you can use colours, mini pictures and lettering to help. When recalling the diagram, you can imagine where each topic is. If there's a gap on the page, you know you've forgotten something. For delivering speeches, talk about each topic in a clockwise order around the page.

Exercise 31 MEMORIZING A DECK OF CARDS

Recalling each card in a shuffled pack is difficult but possible with practice.

Start with a small handful of playing cards and use your creativity to link each one to a friend or celebrity (for example, the King of Clubs might be a nightclub owner or frequenter you know). Now go through the cards in order and 'meet' each of these people in a different place on an imaginary journey – perhaps on your usual walk to work. Over time, increase the number of cards up to a full deck.

Exercise 32 CONSONANT SYSTEM

You can remember large figures, such as telephone numbers, by converting the digits into consonant sounds, as in the example below.

0 = s or z	5 = l
1 = d, t or th	6 = sh or ch
2 = n	7 = g, ng or k
3 = m	8 = f or v
4 = r	9 = p or b

Use memory tricks to link each letter or sound – for example, z(ero) = 0. To remember that David's phone number is 974650 (b-k-r-ch-l-s), imagine him dressed as a BiKeR riding around London's famous CHeLSea area. To recall his phone number, remember 'Biker Chelsea' and do the opposite conversion.

Puzzle 49 CREAM OF THE CROP

Three friends share the same birthday but are lucky enough to be given a cake each. How much can you remember about the cakes? Study the images below for one minute only, then see if you can answer the questions that follow on page 184.

Puzzle 50 ADD AND REMEMBER

This calculator was thrown in the reject pile at the factory. Look closely at it for two minutes and see how many questions you can answer on page 185.

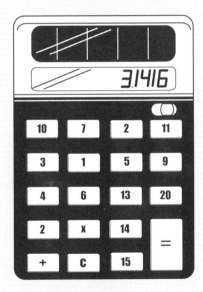

Puzzle 49 CREAM OF THE CROP QUESTIONS

Can you answer these questions about the image on page 182 without looking back?

1 Which cake has the most candles? . . . .

2 How many does it have? . . . .

3 How many curved orange segments are facing leftward on the right-hand cake? . . . .

4 Which cake is the only one to sit on a plate? . . . .

5 How many flowers are there showing on the middle cake? . . . .

6 What's the total number of candles on the left and middle cakes? . . . .

7 How many lines of icing are there on the cake on the left? . . . .

8 How many columns of orange segments feature on the right-hand cake? . . . .

9 How many segments are in each column? . . . .

10 Which two cakes have the same number of candles on each? . . . .

Puzzle 50 ADD AND REMEMBER QUESTIONS
Can you answer these questions about the image on page 183 without looking back?

1 What number appears on the top left key of the calculator?. . . . .

2 Which row of keys contains only odd numbers? . . . . . .

3 What is the only number between one and ten that doesn't appear on the calculator? . . . .

4 What is the answer to the sum on the second row from the bottom? . . . .

5 The only number to appear twice on the keys is? . . . . .

6 What are the last two digits to appear on the answer screen? . . . .

7 What's the sum of all the figures on the top row?. . . . .

8 What is the only number between 10 and 15 that doesn't appear on the calculator? . . . .

9 Name all the numbers and symbols in the first column, from top to bottom . . . .

10 How many digits appear in the answer screen?. . . . . . .

Exercise 33 REVIEW AND REVISE

Even when you find yourself starting to use memory systems, it's important to review the material regularly. The brain forgets things at an exponential rate, which means that the speed at which it starts leaking information increases over time.

One technique is to revise material you have learnt after an hour, a day, a week, a month and a year. This will enable you to retain about 80 per cent of the information. Be sure also to employ your new-found skills wherever possible – what lists, stories, speeches and task lists can you now convert into your preferred memory systems?

BRAIN WORKOUT

You've done your warm-up exercises and now you're
ready for the main mental gymnastics event.
On the pages that follow you'll find a complete
brain-flexing workout comprising all types of puzzles,
from easy through to fiendishly difficult.
Now let's see if all that training has paid off!

The main event

As you will have discovered by now, doing and, most importantly, enjoying puzzles, is one of the best ways to train your brain. So as well as practising the exercises included earlier, set aside time for this section, the ultimate brain workout. The puzzles are graded from one to five bars to give you an indication of the difficulty level, though you may find some of the harder puzzles easier to solve according to your strengths, which may well have changed since you opened this book.

One way to tackle the puzzles is to set yourself time limits. Time yourself doing the puzzle first (use a pencil, or even photocopy the pages if you can) then aim to complete it faster next time. As you start to develop a natural puzzling ability your brain will become swifter and you'll become bolder as you learn new techniques. That's a promise!

A last point to remember is that when you really can't get any further, it's fine to look at the answer. But if you do, take something from it. Try to see how the answer was reached and learn something you can bring to the next puzzle.

Puzzle 51 KAKURO

To complete this Kakuro puzzle, place a single-digit number in each of the white squares so that the two-, three- or four-digit numbers in each row and column add up to the totals shown in the dark squares. No digit may be repeated twice in one number, and some numbers are in place to get you started. This puzzle requires sound logical reasoning.

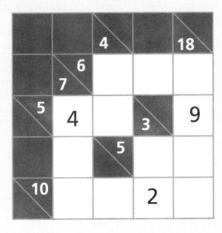

189

Puzzle 52 FIT THE FIGURES

All of these numbers will fit into the grid but patience and numerical thinking are needed. The question is whether you can work out what goes where as there is only one solution. If you take a wrong turning, you'll have to start over again. One number has already been placed to get you started.

3 Digits	5 Digits	7 Digits
564	12778	3232948
587	18207	3645325
825	~~24335~~	3799387
826	26401	3814762
849	29189	3828891
995	47238	5922348
	54563	6592343
4 Digits	59535	6701855
2083	72168	7582412
2143	93973	8101743
3795		9286669
3963	**6 Digits**	9435373
5433	682484	9469155
5648	758341	9548051
9241	826577	
9792	963497	

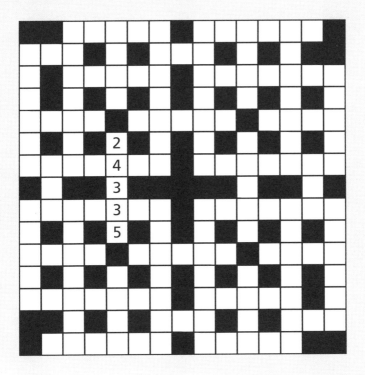

Puzzle 53 BIRTHDAY POOCH

Calling all logical thinkers! Now that you've practised and developed an understanding of the joys of a logical approach to life, can you unravel the information contained in these four simple clues to complete the grid? If so, you'll discover what each of Mrs Tingle's pampered pooches, all of whom share a birthday, received as presents. And can you deduce each breed? (**Hint**: turn to page 35 if you need some tips to get you started.)

CLUES
1 Banjo, a Yorkie, didn't get a bowl.
2 Gifts for Mambo are always red, but he doesn't like bones.
3 The blue ball wasn't for Ringo.
4 The yellow gift wasn't for the poodle.

	YORKIE	POODLE	SCOTTIE	RED	BLUE	YELLOW	BALL	BONE	BOWL
BANJO									
RINGO									
MAMBO									
BALL									
BONE									
BOWL									
RED									
BLUE									
YELLOW									

Puzzle 54 DOUBLE TROUBLE

This puzzle takes twice the effort. First, you need to unravel the letters contained within each of the number groups below, based on the series: v = 1, w = 2, x = 3, y = 4, z = 5, a = 6, b = 7 etc. Then rearrange the letters to spell a series of words. What do they all have in common? Can you do this puzzle in under three minutes?

4 8 10 10 14 16 18 18 20 24 26

17 20 21 25 26

6 7 7 14 18

6 8 9 9 9 16 17 19 20 26

Puzzle 55 THE SECRET SPY

Can you find the spy lurking in this wordsearch? Blowing his cover will help hone your skills of perception and develop the parts of your brain that work with language.

F	O	M	N	M	I	L	B	A	L	F	A
H	A	S	J	K	D	M	S	O	E	R	M
J	P	N	D	K	A	K	H	J	O	D	L
U	N	O	X	E	D	I	B	U	M	E	P
H	D	U	N	D	G	O	E	S	P	S	O
E	J	Y	O	S	Y	U	G	E	J	W	O
D	D	T	N	W	U	S	O	E	N	A	X
T	A	G	J	I	Q	D	P	T	H	Q	S
E	T	F	D	W	H	G	N	E	B	O	G
O	H	P	E	N	N	E	Q	O	G	A	E
M	E	L	H	N	H	T	W	F	B	S	F
O	B	A	D	E	N	F	N	R	E	W	P

Puzzle 56 SHAPE-SHIFTER

What happens to the first shape to turn it into the second shape? Using that knowledge, which of the five options below shows the correct transformation of the next shape?

 is to:

as: **is to:**

a b c d e

Puzzle 57 TRICKY PYRAMID
The usual rules apply for this number pyramid: each brick is equal to the sum of the two bricks below it. However, filling in the gaps here will take a bit of mathematical know-how.

Hint: try a bit of algebra.

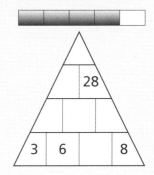

Puzzle 58 ULTIMATE PYRAMID
On this occasion, to get the value of a brick you need to multiply the bricks below it. It may not be as straightforward as it seems.

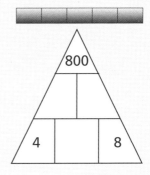

Puzzle 59 DAYTIME SCENE

Relax! It's good for the memory. Examine this pastoral scene for one minute, then try to answer the questions on page 200.

Puzzle 60 NIGHTTIME SCENE

Another scene to grab you. Study this peaceful night scene for two minutes, then tackle the questions on page 201.

Puzzle 59 DAYTIME SCENE QUESTIONS

Can you answer these questions about the image on page 198 without looking back?

1 How many clouds appear in the sky? . . . .

2 How many cows are there? . . . .

3 In which direction is the cow in the background facing? . . . .

4 And in which direction is cow to the left of the picture facing? . . . .

5 How many striped fields are there? . . . .

6 And how many spotty fields are there? . . . .

7 How many cows are standing in the field nearest to the viewer? . . . .

8 How many dark stripes are showing in the nearest field? . . . .

9 And how many light? . . . .

10 How many dark stripes are there altogether? . . . .

Puzzle 60 NIGHTTIME SCENE QUESTIONS

And can you answer these questions about the image on page 199, again without looking back?

1 How many stars are in the sky?. . . . .

2 Across how many fields does the path cut?. . . . .

3 Which way is the crescent moon facing?. . . . .

4 How many houses are there? . . . .

5 Which is the only house with a triangular roof?. . . . . .

6 How many windows does that house have? . . . .

7 Are any of the houses without windows? . . . .

8 How many trees are there altogether?. . . . .

9 How many trees stand alone? . . . .

10 Is the path straight, or does it meander from side
    to side? . . . .

Puzzle 61 BALANCING ACT

Let your mathematical juices flow as you work out how many knives are needed to balance the spoons and forks in scale c, based on the information contained in scales a and b.

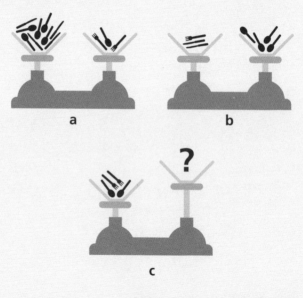

a

b

c

Puzzle 62 SHAPE UP

Test your visual and numerical skills. The value of each shape is the number of its sides multiplied by the number within it. So a square with the number 4 has a value of 16. Find a block two squares wide and two squares high with a total value of exactly 100. Can you do it without putting pen to paper?

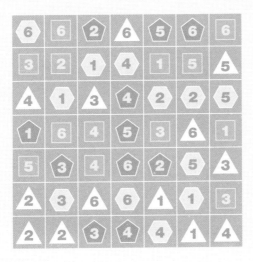

Puzzle 63 DIVIDE AND CONQUER

Can you divide this square into four equal parts, each containing one each of the different shapes? Try to do it first in your mind, before using a pencil, for a real visual challange.

Puzzle 64 LANGUAGE BARRIER IV

Ooh la la! Here's another linguistic code-breaker to test your powers of deduction.

If Gaultier is KOIBDYAN,

Chanel is FLORAB

and Fendi is PARTY …

then who are

KIFFY, BOINAR

and LYBPYKAN?

Puzzle 65 WINDOW BOXES

Bring together your powers of deduction and perception to uncover the missing shape.

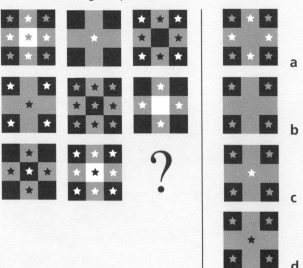

Puzzle 66 JUMBLED UP

Take a look at this jumble of five-figure numbers. Which is the only one to appear just twice? This tests your memory, your perceptiveness, and above all your patience!

86354   45386   34568
34586   53486   68543
68543   34685   86354
34856   68534   34856
86354   86345   35468
35486   34856   35486   35486
45386   43586   53486
34586   35468
53486   43586   86345   68534
68534   34568   68543   43586
34568
35468   86345   45386

Puzzle 67 FIGURES INSIDE

For memory fun, study these shapes with numbers for one minute then try to answer the questions on page 210.

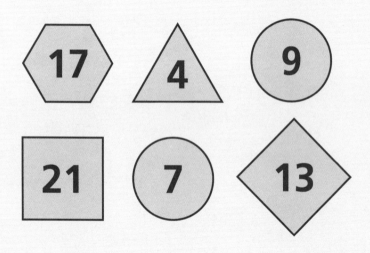

Puzzle 68 NIGHT VISION

Study this street scene for two minutes, then tackle the questions on page 211. This is a difficult puzzle that will test your powers of recall to the maximum.

Puzzle 67 FIGURES INSIDE QUESTIONS

The following questions relate back to the memory puzzle on page 208.

1 Which shape is repeated twice?. . . . .

2 Which is the one shape with an even number inside it?
. . . .

3 Add together the two numbers in the first column. What do you get?. . . . .

4 Which shape has a 13 inside it? . . . .

5 How many sides has the shape with a 17 inside it?. . . .

6 How many straight sides do the shapes in the top row have?. . . . .

7 And in the bottom row? . . . .

8 Which is the biggest number within the shapes?. . . . . .

9 Add together the numbers in the four corners. What do you get?. . . . .

10 How many shapes have four sides?. . . . .

Puzzle 68 NIGHT VISION QUESTIONS

Can you answer these questions about the image on page 209 without looking back?

1 How many lampposts are there? . . . .

2 How many lights does each lamppost have? . . . .

3 Which lamppost has a smaller base than the others?

. . . .

4 How many buildings can you see? . . . .

5 Which lamppost is missing its middle peaked top? . . . .

6 Does the left-hand building have a domed or flat roof?

. . . .

7 Is there a full moon or a crescent moon in the sky?

. . . .

8 How many stars can you see? . . . .

9 How many rows of lights are there on the right-hand building? . . . .

10 How many lights can you see in the left-hand building?

. . . .

Puzzle 69 ELUSIVE MILLIONS

By now you should be at ease with numerical challenges, so try to find the number 9,372,723. It can be found once and once only in the grid. It may be read up, down, forward or backwards, or even diagonally, but it is in there somewhere.

7	9	9	3	7	2	7	3	2	9	2	9
9	3	3	3	3	2	3	9	2	3	3	3
2	7	7	9	7	7	3	9	3	7	2	7
7	2	3	3	3	2	9	2	7	2	3	2
3	7	7	7	9	3	7	3	3	7	7	7
7	2	2	2	2	3	2	2	9	2	2	3
3	2	3	7	3	2	2	7	2	2	7	3
7	3	7	2	7	9	7	9	2	7	3	9
2	7	2	2	7	9	3	3	3	7	9	9
9	3	7	2	3	7	9	9	2	2	3	3
2	3	3	7	9	2	2	7	2	7	3	9
9	2	9	3	2	3	7	2	3	7	2	3

Puzzle 70 PLUG THE GAPS

In this Sudoku grid, each column, row and box of nine squares should contain all the numbers from 1 to 9. Can you fill in the blanks to complete the puzzle? As well as increasing your confidence with number puzzles, this will test the limits of your perseverance as it's easy to go down the wrong path. If you do, it's usually best to start again from scratch.

1	7	3	2				4	9
5		8		4	6	2		
		6		7	9		5	8
4	1			6				7
				1	3	8	9	
3	8	9	5		7	4		
7	6		8		4			2
		2		9	1	5	6	
	5			3				1

Puzzle 71 DOMINO KNOW-HOW

A complete set of dominoes has been randomly laid out within the rectangular grid opposite. By a process of trial and error and using your powers of deduction, can you draw in the edges of the dominoes to work out the position of each within the grid? **Hint**: Tick off each domino below as you 'use' it to help you keep track.

0 • 0	1 • 4	3 • 5
0 • 1	1 • 5	3 • 6
0 • 2	1 • 6	4 • 4
0 • 3	2 • 2	4 • 5
0 • 4	2 • 3	4 • 6
0 • 5	2 • 4	5 • 5
0 • 6	2 • 5	5 • 6
1 • 1	2 • 6	6 • 6
1 • 2	3 • 3	
1 • 3	3 • 4	

3	2	6	1	6	6	3
0	6	5	3	6	0	2
1	0	6	2	5	2	3
1	2	4	0	3	5	1
4	4	1	0	1	3	4
2	6	6	4	2	3	0
2	4	1	3	5	5	1
5	4	5	4	0	5	0

Puzzle 72 BIRD'S EYE VIEW

Pull together your perceptual and lateral thinking skills to discover how this arrangement of shapes would look as seen from above. To make it even harder, the options you've given may have been turned 90 or even 180 degrees …

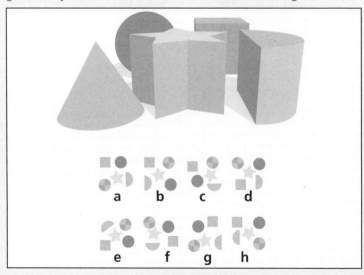

Puzzle 73 SYMBOL SUDOKU

Here's a great puzzle to finish off. This Sudoku-type grid is unique because instead of numbers it uses symbols, so you'll need to work that bit harder to complete it. Each column, row and box of nine squares should contain nine different symbols. Can you fill in the blanks and complete it?

∝		▽		☆				⊖
吕	△		⊙	⊖		☆	ᵫ	
			ᴗ		吕	▽		
	ᵫ					∝		
⊙	吕		▽	ᵫ		ᴗ	△	
ᴗ		⊖			∝	⊙		ᵫ
△		⊙		▽			吕	ᴗ
	ᴗ	☆	吕	△		⊖		
⊖	▽		∝		ᵫ		☆	⊙

217

THE ANSWERS

Puzzle 1 NUMBER PYRAMID

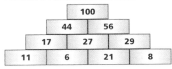

Puzzle 2 WORD POWER

homer simpson

Puzzle 3 SPOT THE DIFFERENCE

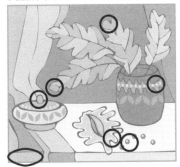

Puzzle 4 TIME TO EAT?
Jerry has a cheese sandwich (clue 1). Thus, the child with both a ham sandwich and an orange drink cannot be Jerry (clue 2) and it isn't Julie (2), so it must be John. The child with a lemon drink isn't Jerry (1), so it must be Julie. By a process of elimination, Jerry has a lime drink and Julie has a chicken sandwich. So: John: ham sandwich, orange drink; Julie: chicken sandwich, lemon drink; Jerry: cheese sandwich, lime drink.

Puzzle 5 HARNESS YOUR EYES
B. The top figure turns 45 degrees and moves to the right side. The middle figure decreases in size and moves inside the bottom figure.

Puzzle 6 HEAP BIG PUZZLE

Puzzle 7 HAMMER HORROR
C (see the pattern on the handle)

Puzzle 8 OPTICAL CHALLENGE
They are all the same size, except C, which is smaller than the others.

Puzzle 9 CUBISM!
B

Puzzle 10 DUPLICATE DRAGONS
A AND D

Puzzle 12 CELEBRITY CONFUSION
1 Jerry Seinfeld
2 Sheryl Crow
3 David Letterman
4 Sarah Michelle Gellar

Puzzle 13 LANGUAGE BARRIER I
QYDW is BACH; QERAK is BIZET;
QZYWTH is BRAHMS.

Puzzle 14 LANGUAGE BARRIER II
A WIVMY is a HONDA; a DEKZIAV
is a CITROEN; a XIKOH is a LOTUS.

Puzzle 15 STEP BY STEP

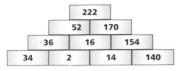

Puzzle 16 CURSE OF THE PHARAOHS

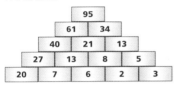

Puzzle 17 WHAT'S NEXT?
180. In each case take the cube of 1, 2, 3 etc. and deduct the square of itself. So $1^3 - 1^2 = 0$, $2^3 - 2^2 = 4$, $3^3 - 3^2 = 18$ etc. $6^3 - 6^2 = 180$.

Puzzle 18 ODD NUMBER OUT
7,289. In each of the others, the first two numbers are added together to give the third or third and fourth numbers; then the second and third numbers are added together to get the rest of the number.

Puzzle 19 SHAPE UP
Most people choose the rounded shape. While curves imply amicable, friendly attributes, linear figures seem cold and unattractive. Is this because organic objects, like human beings, are curved and have no straight lines? This is why, in cartoons, the good guys are curved while baddies often have very pointed, angular faces.

Puzzle 20 NAMING GAME
Did you write 'circle' as one answer? Actually, it's an incomplete circle or an arc. Our brain wants the shape to conform to what it looks like even though it's not really the case. Can you think of similar cases where you've made wrong assumptions?

221

Puzzle 21 STARRY EYED
Try crossing your eyes! Does a third star appear in the middle? Just because only two stars are printed on the page doesn't invalidate the initial statement. Lateral thinking allows us to see what's hidden ...

Puzzle 22 SHAPELY FUN
1 12
2 4
3 4
4 1
5 3
6 Triangle
7 4
8 Circle, circle, square
9 4
10 Triangle

Puzzle 23 A TALL STORY
1 River Phew
2 East Boulder
3 Chuck, Henry and Ivan
4 Chuck
5 8 October
6 Chuck
7 25 minutes (18 + 7)
8 Right
9 Henry, the son
10 Two feet

Puzzle 24 WING IT!
1 Inwards
2 9
3 Smaller
4 3
5 5
6 2
7 Circular
8 Yes
9 12
10 Rounded

Puzzle 25 ROAD SIGN RECALL
1 5
2 4 (6, 120, 24, 12)
3 113 (40 + 6 + 67)
4 3 (67, 5, 71)
5 Yes (8 x 5 = 40)
6 3 (67, 120, 71)
7 3 times (120, 71, 12)
8 79 (8 + 71)
9 3 (6, 5, 8)
10 120; in the middle

Puzzle 26 LOGIC AND SYMBOLS

$$1133$$
$$1 \text{ 🐷} + 2211$$
$$2 \text{ 📺} + 3343$$
$$3 \text{ 🐟} + 4424$$
$$4 \text{ 🥧} = 11111$$

Puzzle 27 SYMBOLS MAZE
The second square in the top row should be your last stop. The arrows show you which direction to move in, and the number of sides on each shape (a circle is taken to have one side) tells you the number of spaces you should move as you travel around the grid.

Puzzle 28 NUMBER JIG AROUND

Puzzle 29 SHOP TILL YOU DROP
The hat that Karen bought is blue (clue 1), and Rose's is brown (3). Phylis bought a red skirt (2), so Sue, who bought a green blouse (4), bought an orange skirt and Patty bought an orange hat. By a process of elimination we can deduce that Phylis bought a green hat and Sue bought a red hat. The skirt that Karen bought is not green (2), so it

must be brown. The blouse Karen bought is not red (2), so it must be orange. The woman with a brown blouse did not buy an orange hat (1), so must have bought a green one. So the woman who bought a blue skirt bought a red blouse, and the woman who bought a blue blouse also bought a green skirt. Rose's blouse isn't red (3), so must be blue. Patty's blouse is red. So:

Karen: orange blouse, blue hat, brown skirt
Patty: red blouse, orange hat, blue skirt
Phylis: brown blouse, green hat, red skirt
Rose: blue blouse, brown hat, green skirt
Sue: green blouse, red hat, orange skirt

Puzzle 30 NOTHING ON EARTH
It's a melted snowman.

Puzzle 31 CAN YOU CANOE?
The woman lent the boys her canoe, giving them a total of 24 canoes. The eldest boy then took half of the 24 boats. ie: 12. The middle child took a third, or 8 canoes. The youngest took an eighth, or 3 canoes. The total number of canoes in the hands of the sons was now 12 + 8 + 3, or 23 canoes, and the tourist was able to reclaim her own canoe and leave with everybody happy.

Puzzle 32 CAKE RING MYSTERY
The baker places five cakes on each side of the scale. If neither group of five is heavier than the other, then the ring is in the eleventh cake. If one of the groups of five is heavier, on the second weigh she puts two each of the cakes from the heavier group on the scales. Again, if they weigh even, the fifth cake contains the ring. If one pair is heavier, she uses her third weigh, placing one

each from the heavier pair on the scales to find which houses her wedding band.

Puzzle 33 JOLLY ODD SHAPES
A is a drummer in a phone booth.
B is a panda taking a bath.
C is a deer hiding behind a bush.
D represents two dice in a pot.
E shows the last spoon of cereal.
F is an igloo with a satellite dish.

Puzzle 34 LATERAL ARCHITECT
In total, 22 cubes have to be added to complete the cube.

Puzzle 35 VISION & INTUITION
There are 21 shapes. What about grouping together the shapes into small sets of five then guessing the number of sets there are? Or guessing the number of each shape then totalling them up? Market traders become extremely accurate at this kind of estimation.

Puzzle 36 INTERSECT
There are 16 intersections. Could you imagine the interactions as glowing red spots? Could you train your brain to tune out and ignore the irrelevant lines?

Puzzle 37 SUM IT UP
a 20; b 29; c 47; d 34; e 55; f 244

Puzzle 38 Z TO A
a 1; b 0; c 2; d 0; e 1; f 1

Exercise 1 LEFT/RIGHT-BRAIN

1	L	**9**	R	**17**	L	**25**	L
2	L	**10**	L	**18**	R	**26**	L
3	L	**11**	L	**19**	R	**27**	R
4	R	**12**	R	**20**	R	**28**	R
5	R	**13**	R	**21**	L	**29**	L
6	R	**14**	L	**22**	R	**30**	R
7	R	**15**	R	**23**	R	**31**	R
8	L	**16**	L	**24**	L	**32**	L

Exercise 3 ONLY ODDITY?
In fact, the only one that isn't the odd one out is the third shape as

there's nothing unique about it – and therefore it's the odd one out. However, somehow it commands the least attention.

Exercise 4 ROUTE MASTER
Those good at perception and clarity might come up with one of the better answers such as 'Turn left at every junction'.

Puzzle 39 NUMBER BREAKDOWN

	1				2		3
				3		1	
		2	4	4			
	1						
		2				2	
				4			
3			3			1	
		4					

Puzzle 40 SCENIC SURPRISE

Puzzle 41 SEW EASY?
1c, 2b, 3a

Puzzle 42 CHICKEN AND EGG
D. Each vertical and horizontal line contains one duck facing right and two facing left. Each vertical and horizontal line contains one white egg, one grey egg, and one picture with no egg. Each vertical and horizontal line contains one duck with a worm and two without. The missing

226

image should therefore be of a duck facing left with a white egg and no worm, so must be d.

Exercise 13
NIGHT FRIGHT ON THE DOORSTEP
Correct spellings are as follows: horrendous, received, minuscule, cemetery, weird, battalion, desperate, sustenance, development, coolly, recommend, irresistible, bowl.

Exercise 14 ONE IN THREE
1 accommodate   **5** exceed
2 millennium   **6** inoculate
3 harass   **7** memento
4 consensus   **8** repetition

Exercise 16
WHEELBARROW WORDS
First handle: gardener
Second handle: lawnmower
One wheel: hosepipe
Other wheel: sprinkler
End rim: spade

Puzzle 43 MISSING PRESIDENTS

C	A	R	T	E	R
H	O	O	V	E	R
A	R	T	H	U	R
M	O	N	R	O	E
R	E	A	G	A	N
W	I	L	S	O	N

Puzzle 44 LANGUAGE BARRIER III
TIVAK is MONET; TYKEHHA is MATISSE; JAPYH is DEGAS.

Puzzle 45 NUMBER DIVIDER
19

Puzzle 46 WEIGH IT UP
14. Substitute T for triangle, C for circle, and S for square to reach the following:

a: $T + 2C = S$
b: $3T = 6C + S$

Substituting a into b gives:
$$3T = 6C + T + 2C$$
So $3T = 8C + T$
So $2T = 8C$
Therefore $T = 4C$

Substituting this information into scale a gives:
$$S = 4C + 2C$$
So $S = 6C$

Using all this information we can therefore work out that scale c equals:
$(2 \times 4C) + 6C = 8C + 6C = 14C$.
So 14 is the answer.

Puzzle 47 HIDDEN NUMBER

5	3	5	5	3	5	9	7	1	9	2	5
9	5	5	3	3	5	7	9	2	8	5	3
2	7	3	5	7	3	1	9	2	3	5	5
7	8	2	3	3	2	9	2	9	2	3	2
3	7	9	7	9	9	7	1	2	3	2	5
2	2	1	1	2	1	7	9	9	3	9	7
3	2	8	9	3	9	2	7	2	2	5	9
5	3	4	2	2	7	2	9	1	7	1	5
5	7	6	3	3	9	3	3	2	7	9	2
9	3	5	5	3	7	9	9	5	3	3	3
2	5	5	5	9	2	2	7	4	5	5	5
5	5	3	2	9	7	1	1	2	3	5	5

Puzzle 48 FUN WITH NUMBERS

19	–	10	x	20	+	32	=	212
+		x		+		–		
10	x	19	–	32	+	20	=	178
x		–		x		+		
32	–	20	x	10	+	19	=	139
–		+		–		x		
20	+	32	–	19	x	10	=	330
=		=		=		=		
908		202		501		310		

Puzzle 49 CREAM OF THE CROP

1. The cake in the middle
2. 9
3. 5
4. The left-hand cake
5. 6
6. 16 (7 + 9)
7. 4
8. 5
9. 2
10. Those on the left and right each have seven candles

Puzzle 50 ADD AND REMEMBER

1. 10
2. Second row from the top (3, 1, 5, 9)
3. 8
4. 28 (2 x 14)
5. 2
6. 1 and 6
7. 30 (10 + 7 + 2 + 11)
8. 12
9. 10, 3, 4, 2, +
10. 5 (3.1416)

Puzzle 51 KAKURO

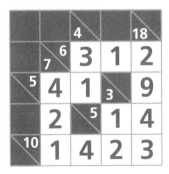

Puzzle 52 FIT THE FIGURES

Puzzle 53 BIRTHDAY POOCH

Banjo is a Yorkie; he did not receive a bowl (1). Mambo's gift was red, but not a bone (2). The ball was blue and not for Ringo (3). The yellow gift was not for the poodle (4). Mambo's red gift, if not a bone (2) or a ball (3) must be a bowl, making the bone yellow. The blue ball is not for Ringo (3) or Mambo (2) so it must have been for Banjo, leaving Ringo the yellow bone. If the Yorkie, Banjo, didn't get the bone or the bowl (1) he must have got the blue ball. Lastly, if Ringo's yellow bone wasn't for the poodle (4) or the Yorkie (Banjo's ball is blue), he must be a Scottie and Mambo is a poodle. So:

Banjo: Yorkie, blue ball
Mambo: poodle, red bowl
Ringo: Scottie, yellow bone

Puzzle 54 DOUBLE TROUBLE

Mickey Mouse   Pluto
Bambi   Donald Duck

They're all characters from Walt Disney cartoons.

Puzzle 55 THE SECRET SPY

F	O	M	N	M	I	L	B	A	L	F	A
H	A	S	J	K	D	M	S	O	E	R	M
J	P	N	D	K	A	K	H	J	O	D	L
U	N	O	X	E	D	I	B	U	M	E	P
H	D	U	N	D	G	O	E	S	P	S	O
E	J	Y	O	S	Y	U	G	E	J	W	O
D	D	T	N	W	U	S	O	E	N	A	X
T	A	G	J	I	Q	**D**	P	T	H	Q	S
E	T	F	D	W	H	**G**	N	E	B	O	G
O	H	P	E	N	N	E	Q	**O**	G	A	E
M	E	L	H	N	H	T	W	**F**	B	S	F
O	B	A	D	E	N	F	N	R	E	W	P

Puzzle 56 SHAPE-SHIFTER

C. The shape in the top middle of the larger shape becomes the new outer shape. The original outer shape moves to the top middle. Any intersecting lines (in this case a cross) move to below the top middle shape. The smallest shape, originally within the top middle shape, moves to the top of the main shape and moves round 180 degrees.

Puzzle 57 TRICKY PYRAMID

The difficulty arises when we try to deduce the value of the third brick in the bottom row. So call it x for now. We therefore know that the second and third bricks in the second row up equal x + 6 and x + 8 respectively. The second brick in the third row up equals 28, and it is the sum of the two bricks below it. Hence we can work out that:

$$28 = (x + 6) + (x + 8)$$
So $28 = 2x + 14$
So $2x = 14$
So $x = 7$

Using this information, we can complete the rest of the pyramid as follows:

231

Puzzle 58 ULTIMATE PYRAMID
We don't know the value of the middle brick in the bottom row, so let's call it a for now. We know therefore that the value of the two bricks in the middle row must equal 4a and 8a respectively. So 4a x 8a = 800. This means that $32a^2 = 800$. So $a^2 = 25$. Therefore a = 5. We can then go on to complete the pyramid as follows:

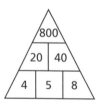

Puzzle 59 DAYTIME SCENE

1 15	**5** 2	**9** 5
2 3	**6** 1	**10** 10
3 Right	**7** 2	
4 Left	**8** 5	

Puzzle 60 NIGHTTIME SCENE

1 23	**6** 2
2 4	**7** The middle house has only a door
3 Right	
4 3	
5 The house on the left-hand side	**8** 11
	9 3
	10 It meanders

Puzzle 61 BALANCING ACT
16. Work it out as follows. Scale a gives us:
$$4k + 5s = 2f + 1s$$
$$So \quad 2f = 4k + 4s$$

Scale b gives us:
$$2k + 1f = 4s$$

Substitute the value of 4s from scale b into scale a to get:

$$2f = 4k + 2k + 1f$$
$$2f = 6k + 1f$$
$$So \quad 1f = 6k$$

Substituting this into scale b gives:

2k + 6k = 4s
8k = 4s

So   1s = 2k

Substituting these values for forks and spoons into scale c tells us that:

2s = 4k
2f = 12k

So we need 16 knives to balance scale c.

Puzzle 62 SHAPE UP

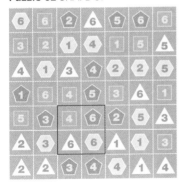

Puzzle 63 DIVIDE AND CONQUER

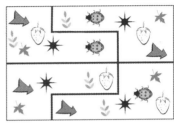

Puzzle 64 LANGUAGE BARRIER IV
KIFFY is GUCCI; BOINAR is LAUREN; LYBPYKAN is HILFIGER.

Puzzle 65 WINDOW BOXES
B. Each vertical and horizontal line contains a grey, a white, and a black central square. Each line contains a grey, a white and a black central star. Each line contains an image with four grey corner stars, one with white and one with black. Each line contains one set of top, bottom and side grey squares, one with white, and one with black. The missing

image should therefore have a grey central square, a grey central star, four grey corner stars, and four grey top, bottom and side stars.

Puzzle 66 JUMBLED UP
34586

Puzzle 67 FIGURES INSIDE
1 Circle
2 Triangle
3 17 + 21 = 38
4 Diamond
5 6
6 9
7 8
8 21
9 17 + 9 + 21 + 13 = 60
10 2: the square and diamond

Puzzle 68 NIGHT VISION
1 4
2 3
3 Second from the right
4 2
5 The first one
6 Domed
7 Full moon
8 None
9 4 rows
10 20

Puzzle 69 ELUSIVE MILLIONS

7	9	9	3	7	2	7	3	2	9	2	9
9	3	3	3	3	2	3	9	2	3	3	3
2	7	7	9	7	7	3	9	3	7	2	7
7	2	3	3	3	2	9	2	7	2	3	2
3	7	7	7	9	3	7	3	3	7	7	7
7	2	2	2	2	3	2	2	9	2	2	3
3	2	3	7	3	2	2	7	2	2	7	3
7	3	7	2	7	9	7	9	2	7	3	9
2	7	2	2	7	9	3	3	3	7	9	9
9	3	7	2	3	7	9	9	2	2	3	3
2	3	3	7	9	2	2	7	2	7	3	9
9	2	9	3	2	3	7	2	3	7	2	3

Puzzle 70 PLUG THE GAPS

1	7	3	2	8	5	6	4	9
5	9	8	1	4	6	2	7	3
2	4	6	3	7	9	1	5	8
4	1	5	9	6	8	3	2	7
6	2	7	4	1	3	8	9	5
3	8	9	5	2	7	4	1	6
7	6	1	8	5	4	9	3	2
8	3	2	7	9	1	5	6	4
9	5	4	6	3	2	7	8	1

Puzzle 71 DOMINO KNOW-HOW

Puzzle 72 BIRD'S EYE VIEW

F

Puzzle 73 SYMBOL SUDOKU

∝	⊙	▽	⋃	☆	△	유	⊔	▽
유	△	⊔	⊙	▽	▽	☆	⋃	∝
☆	▽	⋃	⊔	∝	유	▽	⊙	△
▽	⋃	△	☆	⊙	⊔	∝	▽	유
⊙	유	∝	▽	⋃	▽	⊔	△	☆
⊔	☆	▽	△	유	∝	⊙	▽	⋃
△	∝	⊙	▽	▽	☆	⋃	유	⊔
⋃	⊔	☆	유	△	⊙	▽	∝	▽
▽	▽	유	∝	⊔	⋃	△	☆	⊙

The Brain Box Impossible Cube

You will have noticed a wooden cube puzzle in your Brain Box. This cube is a great way of testing all you have learned about logical thinking, intuition, patience and perseverance, as well as the importance of never being scared to make mistakes as part of the learning process.

First unravel the cube so it looks like the image shown below. Note the swivelling action of the small cubes. This is the key movement you'll need to use as you re-assemble the cube. Do not force the cubes in any other direction.

Suggested Reading

Alice's Adventures in Wonderland by Lewis Carroll. Penguin, 1994.

The Art of Seeing by Aldous Huxley. Flamingo, 1994.

An Autobiography or The Story of My Experiments with Truth by M. K. Ghandi. Penguin, 1982.

Best Mathematical Puzzles by Sam Loyd. Dover, 2000.

The Brain: A Very Short Introduction by Michael O'Shea. Oxford University Press, 2005.

The Brain Book by Peter Russell. Routledge, 1979.

Edward de Bono's Thinking Course by Edward de Bono. BBC Books, 2004.

The Eureka Effect: The Art and Logic of Breakthrough Thinking by David Perkins. Norton, 2001.

Humor Works by John Morreall. HRD Press, 1997.

Make the Most of Your Mind by Tony Buzan. Colt Books, 1977.

Meditation by Eknath Easwaran. Nilgiri Press, 1991.

The Mind Map Book: Radiant Thinking – Major Evolution in Human Thought by Tony & Barry Buzan. BBC Books, 2003.

The Number Devil by Hans Magnus Enzensberger. Granta Books, 2000.

The Oxford Guide to Word Games by Tony Augarde. Oxford University Press, new edition 2003.

Penguin Book of Word Games by David Parlett. Penguin, 1982.

The Phantom Tollbooth by Norton Juster. Epstein & Carroll Associates, 1961.

BOOKINABOX

Editorial Director Ian Jackson
Art Director Elaine Partington
Mac Designer Malcolm Smythe
Production Cara Herron

IMagine Puzzles Ltd

Editor Ali Moore
Art Editor Keith Miller
Proofreader Sarah Barlow

Puzzle providers

David Bodycombe, Moran Campbell da Vinci, Edward Phantera,
Probyn Puzzles.

brainbox@librios.com

Clipart

Nova Development Corporation and Hemera Technologies Inc.

Charles Phillips would like to thank his brain-trainers,
Alison, Melanie, Jim and Tom, who keep his neurons firing
by surprising him every day.